THE GHOSTS OF MALTA

JOSEPH ATTARD

Publishers Enterprises Group (PEG) Ltd

Publishers Enterprises Group (PEG) Ltd
P.E.G. Building, UB7, Industrial Estate,
San Gwann SGN 09,
Malta

First edition 1983
Reprinted with additions 1990, 1994, 1995, 1997

ISBN: 99909-0-030-2

Photoset and printed in Malta by P.E.G. Ltd.

Biographical Note

Joseph Attard was born in Vittoriosa and received his education at the Malta Lyceum and The Royal University of Malta. He entered the Civil Service to make a brilliant career. Nevertheless his heart was always in the art of writing which he cultivated since his early formative years. His first successes in this field were in free-lance journalism and short-story writing for the English press in the fifties, when he was also given two foreign assignments with UNESCO. His first novel *I Chased a Ghost* was published in the United Kingdom in 1968.

This was followed by *Oleanders in the Wind*. But as if to establish his equal versatility with his own language, Joseph Attard then wrote four books in Maltese – *It-Toroq Kollha Jwasslu għall-Ruma (All Roads Lead to Rome), Taħt is-Sinjal ta' Taurus (Under the Sign of Taurus), Ix-Xitan Wasal fit-Tlettax (The Devil Came on the Thirteenth), L-Aħħar Appuntament (Last Appointment).* His next book *the Battle of Malta* was a best-seller. It was published in hardback by William Kimber in 1980 and in two paperback editions in 1982. After that there were *The Ghosts of Malta, Industrial Relations in Malta, Britain and Malta – The Story of an Era*, another best-seller, *The Atlantis Inheritance, The Angel of Death*, *The Knights of Malta,* and *The Struggle for the Mediterranean.*

He has also written several radio plays as well as a television serial. Joseph Attard who lives at Balzan is married and has three children.

By the same author

In English

I Chased a Ghost
Oleanders in the Wind
The Battle of Malta
The Ghosts of Malta (1st Edition)
Industrial Relations in Malta
Britain and Malta – The Story of an Era
The Atlantis Inheritance
The Angel of Death
The Knights of Malta
The Struggle for the Mediterranean

In Maltese

It-Toroq Kollha Jwasslu għall-Ruma (*All Roads Lead to Rome*)
Taħt is-Sinjal ta' Taurus (*Under the Sign of Taurus*)
Ix-Xitan Wasal fit-Tlettax (*The Devil Came on the Thirteenth*)
L-Aħħar Appuntament (*Last Appointment*)

Contents

Foreword

As I had occasion to mention in the foreword to the previous and first edition of this book, I cannot deny having always been fascinated by the popular subject of ghosts, but my fascination was never strong enough to compel me to write about them. The more so when I was still sceptical and considered all that was said and written about the occult as being nonsense and fiction. Then my attitude took a severe beating when I suddenly had to assist at situations in which the incidence of ghosts became obvious. It was this series of extraordinary situations and which were included in the first edition that had first imbued me with the desire to know more about the world of ghosts, and this was what eventually brought me in contact with those of Malta.

The fact that all this came at a time when my country was making new history that had to be recorded threatened to put me off course with my being prone to write of a country's achievements rather than its ghosts. But it was here that I could not help notice the close connection that existed between Malta's ghosts and her history. As I delved into records and information of times long gone by in search of material, there were the colourful episodes of the island's history being unfolded, all of them unmistakably marked with fantastic occurrances that found reflection in the occult. Some of these in turn helped to bring to light historical elements which were never recorded thus bringing meaning where it was lacking. It soon became obvious that the two subjects were not such as to be studied in isolation of each other.

However, no man can sit down to write on such a dubious and frail subject of the past without bringing to task what misconceptions and arguments are bound to spring out of the present. Particularly when this belongs to a new generation which believes in what is more material than ghosts. There were also to be considered the new times with post-war Malta busily changing her role from time immemorial that of a fortress into one of a peaceful industrialized nation. Her transformation into a republic and the departure of the British garrison after a 180 year stay followed. All of these being events far detached from the world of ghosts, yet so important to substantiate or discredit the fantastic beliefs that were born with my first involvement by the argument that if ghosts really existed in past history they would be expected to feature in the new one.

The book was therefore cast, in the form of a historical narrative which was interrupted to relate stories and facts that would bring my theme into focus. And this theme was not history, but ghosts. Of the same types that were to be found in stories of many lands; also ghosts that were particular to Malta and with their time ranging from centuries ago right to the very days when the book was first published in May, 1982.

It had never crossed my mind to cast myself as some expert on ghosts or the occult, and I wrote this book without any particular theory to argue. Whatever theories I had proposed were made in good faith for whoever wanted to use them. But it must be said that however disputable some of the mentioned manifestations may have seemed, there was beneath them all a solid substream of fact and authenticity.

If there was proof needed of the ever growing interests in the subject of ghosts this came through the numerous readers of my first book who contacted me or my publishers with positive comments. The whole edition was completely sold out in no time and there were soon the clamourings for a second one. Had I given heed to the many inevitable readers who came forward with stories of their own to relate I would have had to restructure the whole book and in the process retrace my steps into past history already covered. So rather than doing this I chose to stick to the first edition and add a new chapter to cover more recent manifestations of the ghosts of Malta since then. Besides updating my records this would go a long way to provide continuity and confirmation to the feeling expressed at the end of the book that other than its blue skies, the wonderful history, and warm friendliness as top attractions, Malta will always have her ghosts.

It only remains to me to re-endorse my gratitude and appreciation to the authors and publishers who allowed me to draw on their publications in the first place and to thank all those, whether mentioned by their real name or not, who had volunteered information for both editions of the book.

Malta
1st April 1990

Joseph Attard

Prologue

As in the late afternoon the sun sinks behind the horizon in the West, the sky is low, of unbroken leaden blue soon to become black. Very often a light breeze would rustle through the abundant oleanders in the gardens on the bastions round Grand Harbour, whispering the approach of evening. It is now that their white, pink and red blossoms would lose their colour as they droop in obedience to the coming night. The tall conifers and pines would then also stare like disapproving old men at the watery domain below. The harbour will then look like a thin steel ring, twisted in places where the creeks are, with their hazy contours looking more like some retaining walls keeping back from overflowing into the placid waters the crowded buildings of the cities, already laying in the shadow of the darkening sky against which only the belfries and cupolas of churches stand out.

In the middle of the harbour lies the predominant edifice of Fort St Angelo. An exhibition of might and splendour, with its bastions, ravelins and vedettes so graceful in the sunny daylight, now looking like a frozen explosion of granite with its lines undefined in the quickly falling darkness.

Pinpoints of light will however soon twinkle to relieve the picture as the night is in full descent; and as the panorama becomes like a sea of myriad lights there seems to rise the same sigh of a century before when people would have welcomed even their then poor illuminations as they abandoned the roads and huried home – before the ghosts would walk.

Many of those roads have today disappeared as towns and villages that contained them have expanded to leave much less of the manless tracks and paths across deserted countryside. What few are left do no longer look derelict, embellished as they are with asphalt and lights. Only the holy niches remain to remind all of the times when they were erected as a safeguard and protection from spectral dogs, two headed cats or animated balls of mist that haunted those spots. Those were the domestic hauntings of the roads by the sort of ghost that might have belonged to someone meeting a violent death at that place; but the fascination of ghosts in Malta goes much deeper. The island bubbles with history and mystery. Within the cities that have just been seen disappearing in the shadows of falling night, many a husband and wife would at a similar time of a century back be sitting with their children to a frugal dinner by the flickering light of an oil-lamp, when gas was a luxury not much indulged in. They might even have finished their meal and would be saying night prayers in their black oak beamed dining room. But their eyes would often be caught turned to glance beyond the window panes to the courtyard or street outside darkened to a deeper solitude, as if wondering whether it was after all safer out there than facing what the coming night would bring. Apprehension would reach its zenith as the lamps are put out when all would retire to bed. Sleep might not be easy to come by and the spouses would very likely snuggle together, motionless, straining to hear beyond the pounding of their hearts, the sounds that would indicate the presence of the ghost that would come into being.

The first indication might come in the way of heavy breathing close by, or a man's footsteps walking up or down the stairs. There might even be the sound of chains being pulled as if shackled to the walker's feet. Husband and wife would stiffen in fearful expectancy of what they know would normally follow these manifestations.

In cases where the ghost materializes it would take the form of a small turk or a leprechaun who in many cases would resort to playful antics like taking babies from their cot to put them on the floor, or teasing children, asleep or awake, by pulling their hair. He might even annoy the husband or wife, whichever of them he would have attached himself to, or both, and he might even give money to any such protegee. This act of benevolence might very often cause friction and anguish to the married couple since it is always done with the usual established condition that one could not talk about the ghosts one saw, and gifts received. If this condition is not observed then the given money would turn into something worthless, very often into snails, with the protegee getting chastised, by a now turned malevolent ghost.

Such shuddering experiences would have to be endured night after night, and sometimes even during the day, straining nerves and resistence with the imposed forebearance to mention experiences until residence is changed. Only then there would be relief.

This type of haunting had become such a regular practice developing the same psychic pattern that these manifestations perpetrated an individuality to earn the spirit a particular description. The Maltese of a century ago called it *Hares*, a word meaning "protect", but more likely being a derivative of *Lares* which meant house guardian, since it was evident even then that the haunting turk or leprechaun had appointed itself to guard the house it haunted. Inevitably, stories were handed down, gathering more colour and additions, but the *Hares* never lost its fascination to the fantasies of tradition and folk-lore.

It held its place even in confrontation with other types of ghostly manifestations which found provenance in a Christian interpretation of the immortality of the soul and its existence in another spiritual life after death of the body, from where a spirit might return to its earthly habitat to implore prayers or to complete or command some undone task conditioned to its suffrage. In this circumstance the Maltese seem to have found causes and reasons as well for unexplained apparitions in the form of spectral incongruencies or the different types of poltergeist. For the first time they produced answers to the many still unanswered questions featuring in the world of the occult. Their analysis was a very simple one, classifying ghosts in either being good spirits to be placated by prayers for the suffrage they seek, or evil ones to be removed by solemn exorcism.

Little if any is mentioned of the third kind of ghost nurtured by the significance behind haunting, with the word itself being of the same root as "home" and "ham" meaning "homing" which implies that a spirit has remained at or returned to its earthly habitat. This implication which qualifies for a scientific explanation finds credence in the many connections of apparitions in Malta and the island's historical past under the Arabs, Normans, Angevines, Aragonese, Castillians and the Knights of St John. All these had left an impact in the unique cosmopolitan, feudal and religious structure in Maltese culture, still evident today, but under the faces of the beautiful Siculo-Norman architecture and the magnificent Baroque there can still be sensed the cold feeling of suffering and violence that must have paired chivalry and pageantry. The general feeling has always been that some imprint of acts of deep emotion must have been superimposed on the surroundings. The narrow streets of Vittoriosa, deep shadowed between lofty palaces and auberges still express foreboding; Cospicua and Senglea, nestling behind bastions which still reflect the presence of the Ottoman Turks that had once trodden and died there. Valletta, resplendent with Knights' showpieces can still ring to the screaming of some damsel in distress. Mdina, the Siculo-Norman gem, a capital of four centuries ago, still radiates its atmosphere of silence, broken only by the sensed tread of mailed feet. Underneath the sun drenched buildings, everywhere, there lie the dark dungeons, cellars and similarly rock hewn chambers where the many turkish slaves served their despotic masters and died in the very places the *Hares* haunted. This might very well explain the issue.

In the relationship of history there was also the French occupation on 10 June 1798 until the capitulation to the British on 5 September 1800. Both periods added to the incidence of hauntings. Throughout the 164 year British rule then, there must have been many additions to local stories with the inevitable importations of the English type of phantom fantasy as is still prevalent in the British Isles, to distort the local picture making it more attractive, maybe more baffling, but certainly less credible. To all this the Maltese retained their own private judgement in a quality of aloofness – claiming nothing, and denying still less. But opinion never departed from the strong belief that this sector of the occult complemented existing religious belief rather than replaced it, codifying the immortal existence of the soul – a dogma of their dynamic and militant faith. With a benevolent church turning a blind eye upon harmless custom, even though sometimes bordering on pagan survivals, it was no wonder that ghosts, whether in the form of the protecting *Hares*, a returned soul seeking suffrage, a damned poltergeist, or a simple persisting imposition of an emotional death, became an unencumbered and factual element of Maltese life.

It remained so until 1940, when war broke out, and Malta had to face more deadly manifestations than psychic in the daily bombardments it had to endure for three years. In that whirlpool of an existence all that was doubtful and the possible product of fantasy was pulled down into the vortex of tradition. There were included the ghosts that had excited Malta for a decade, and died with the buildings they haunted. These were indeed more than literally obliterated in the devastation that followed.

Then the war was over, bringing with it the sheer physical job of reconstruction, and the rescue of what was left of a shattered civilisation. It was not intended that this should include ghosts. But they returned. Without anybody's will and effort there was the old *Hares* again in buildings that were left; gleaming ladies and haughty knights appeared in historic forts that still stood; monks and priests from another era were back, intent on retribution for suffrage. The white hooded figures of the *Misericordia* were again on the prowl, while physical practices of three years back began to manifest themselves again with the same surviving psychic pattern.

This time however they had to be authentic if they were to withstand the changed and progressive public opinion of the new times which would no longer support an improvable ghost. It was because they were authentic that they converted sceptics, myself included, and challenged research which proved that in the conflageration of paranormal stories, anecdotes and similar products which some attributed to superstition and fantasy there was that which pertained to spirits of the departed manifesting themselves. More than the dramatic, romance, adventure and mystery they provided a challenge to what until now has been considered an impassable barrier to the unknown beyond. Their scattered hauntings could now be researched and supplianted by the same arguments many a time used in explanation by the sceptics. They can now make a coherent whole, no longer wrapped up in the language of the allegory or superstition, but considered in a story of reality and actuality.

This, is the story of the Ghosts of Malta.

Chapter 1

Ghosts and History

When it was dawn, on days following immediately the end of the war in 1945, and dazzling light was falling to shimmer on the blue water of Grand Harbour, Fort St Angelo was again revelling in its mighty glory to be viewed from every coign of vantage. Its lines of stalwart bastions were again well defined with the sun never failing to lend them a pale golden glow. Flashes of colour from its gardens added again a touch of natural beauty to the impregnable magnificence.

But even with the sense of impregnability and protection that the fort was again radiating as if to hint fun of any spectral influences of a past era, it was still carrying, as it had always done, the burden of a haunting ghost. For behind its architectural felicities and traditional air of a sentinel there still lurked the flitting spectre of the Grey Lady.

Throughout British rule, the fortress was rated as a man-of-war. It was in fact called HMS St Angelo, with its storeys becoming "Decks" and its rooms "cabins", all under the command of a Flag Captain who had his quarters in the house of the governor at the top. It was certainly no place for a lone lady, and one must look farther back to trace the origin of the woman whose ghost had persistently haunted the fort right into our times. Indeed, the long dress, and the long pointed head gear and veil in which the ghost always appeared placed her class to an era before the coming of the Knights of St John to Malta in 1530. It was their first Grandmaster L'Isle Adam that between this year and 1534 effected important extensions to the smaller fort to make of it the gem of today. There had also been other extensions carried out during previous occupations, but the first fort knew its origin to Siculo-Norman times when it had its first governor who was a Sicilian Aragonese Captain of the Rod, a member of the noble family of Nava. It was in his time that the ghost came into being.

It is to Captain Eric Brockman that I am indebted for details about the ghost of the Grey Lady which in his book "The Last Bastion" he describes as having been heard, seen, and making her presence felt on countless occasions over the years. She was not bound to any particular place, but there was one room where she was often felt or heard to pass to the accompaniment of all the familiar signs of a cold blast of air, the slowly opening doors, the rustle of voluminous skirts and the light, tapping footfall. All those who saw her, amongst whom there were small children who described her as "the nice lady", said that she was beautiful and sad, but never wept, groaned or screamed.

More interesting than her manifestations is her identification. The Grey Lady was identified to have been one of the two women in the life of the Sicilian Aragonese Captain di Nava. Whether she was his wife or not was never clarified, but what is known is that when on one occasion she tried to call on Di Nava on a day and time which were not convenient for him, presumably because of the company of the other woman, he ordered two of his guards to get rid of her before she could reach him. The poor woman was killed, and her body cast into a convenient dungeon. Since then her ghost had haunted the fort throughout the centuries that followed without respite right into our time. It appears that none of the British captains had ever bothered about her restless spirit, and this might have strengthened certain beliefs that the ghost and its story were English inventions.

This theory seems to have been blown up when for the first time a Maltese wife to an English captain took up residence at the fort and true to Maltese characteristics had masses said for the repose of the restless soul, assuming that it was only after suffrage. Instead of quietening the Grey Lady however, the masses turned her into a poltergeist. She became vulgar and noisy, banging doors and throwing furniture about. It became obvious that hers was not the kind of ghost it was thought to be, and there was only one other alternative to be resorted to. The consort to the succeeding captain happened to be another Maltese and she followed in her predecessor's footsteps in attending to the ghost. This time however she resorted to the alternative of solemn exorcism. The Grey Lady was then never seen or heard again.

Whatever interest this manifestation held had died down after the haunting stopped. There wasn't necessarily the same reaction with the sceptics regarding psychic phenomena who might still have considered this to have been another story. To set them thinking however there was a sequel to the story which came about some years ago when restoration work was being carried out at the fort. On the walls in the room through which the ghostly lady often passed, beneath layers of plaster of indeterminate age, were exposed armorial frescoes amongst which there was that of Di Nava. Beneath this there was also exposed a doorway leading to a stairway which went down into a deep dungeon. At the bottom were found three skeletons – two male and one female. The former might have belonged to the silenced guards. The other skeleton could have been that of the murdered woman, since with it there was some fabric which might have once been grey.

It was easy to arrive at an explanation for this haunting, but there were concurrent occurrances which carried neither logic nor moral significance. They could have been attributed to the imaginary or fraud, but as we know today they could have also been the result of superimposition on a place of the last emotional act of a dying person.

Since childhood I had known fishermen speaking of

weird shrieking sometimes heard on their return from the fishing grounds as they approached the ramparts of Fort Ricasoli at the entrance of Grand Harbour. It was something that could not be attributed to sea gulls since it occurred outside their time and season. It could not be connected to wind or currents finding their way through caverns in the rocky coastline on which the fort stands. Those who were occult minded found a connection however to the spirits of the executed in the time of the Knights of St John, who made a habit of leaving the dead bodies hanging over the ramparts as a lesson and deterrent to others.

It was a likely explanation which might have even found its way in local folklore. But there was no explanation why the shrieks, seemingly coming with the same timbre never varied in a crescendo that seemed to associate them with the screaming of some poor individual falling to his death. They fitted better a particular execution of a Captain General Francesco St Clement who as captain of a flotilla of the Order's galleys, was in 1570 routed and put to flight by the Turkish corsair Luciali off the Tunisian coast. Defeat in battle was a calculated risk with the Knights, particularly in a case like that of St Clement with his galleys poorly manned and equipped. But it was a different case with flight in front of the enemy. This was considered as cowardice which was punishable with an ignominous death by strangling and as if this should not kill, to have the body thrown over the bastions into the sea. This was how St Clement met his death, and the wild sea beneath Fort Ricasoli may for all I know be still echoing his last emotional moment.

There were however manifestations which could mirror their times so faithfully as to fill blanks in details of history. In their case any possibility of imagination or fraud can be ruled out. One exemplifying haunting was that of a ghost which manifested itself at Marsa. This is a small town that stretches from the periphery of Valletta the capital to the towns of the inner harbour area. It has relatively big areas of flat low-lying land with little if any of the usual rocky strata in the surface. Through the ages rain waters flowing thereon from higher ground had deposited soil and earth making the spot an ideal place for constructions requiring flat soft ground. Malta's only racecourse, golf links, tennis courts and the first turf football stadium have all found their ambient there. But Marsa seems to have also received attention from the Turks as far back as 1551 when corsairs under the redoubtable Dragut often landed in Malta on raids and reached as far as that locality. Very likely, being at the far end of Grand Harbour, Marsa offered a bird's eye view of the defences that were to be attended to in the planned siege to be undertaken some years later. These incursions had also afforded them an insight into the use that could be made of those wide open spaces. Indeed, notwithstanding the fact that on the onset of the siege of 1565 the Knights of St John and the Maltese had poisoned the water wells and springs that abounded there, the place was chosen immediately to house a Turkish tent hospital to accommodate their sick and wounded.

A house which lies quite close to where this hospital once stood still stands, looking slightly forelorn, like an aged woman trying to keep her dignity and pride after being out of luck. It shows an air of pathos and gloom. Maybe even of menace. But it is inhabited by normal people. And also by a ghost.

First indications were that of a *Hares*. It later transpired that the ghost was not one of the characteristic little leprechaun, but of a big tough looking turk in his late seventies, dressed in brilliant clothes and turban, and carrying a scimitar in his waistband to combine regality with the bizarre. His steps sounded deft but steady when he walked, and his impatient gait hinted at alertness and agility notwithstanding his old age. I don't known for how long the inhabitants of the house stuck to their guns mesmerised into terror by this apparition. Possibly they refrained from mentioning anything about it because of the conditions of silence associated with the *Hares*. It became a situation wherein they were driven away by the instinct of fear, but were always somehow pulled back by some attraction which they could not live away from or without. They left several times, but succumbed to turn back, always with an increasing feeling of curiosity about the identity of their brilliantly clothed agile ghost. Maybe they were constantly hoping to find him gone, or for all I know they were hopeful to be lead to some cache of money which often featured in hauntings by turks. But neither of these hopes was realised. it was only when silence was broken and the ghostly description reached a local historian that the message was deciphered and the ghost identified through his unique brilliant clothing to have belonged to Dragut.

Dragut Rais was the intelligent and able corsair who spent most of his time fighting and pillaging for Barbarossa. His record of piracy was unequalled, and his captives ran into fantastic numbers which included also Maltese taken during his various raids on Malta. But his biggest and last connection with Malta was during the Great Siege of 1565 when he was placed by Soleyman to impose his brilliant soldiership on the other two turkish commanders Mustapha and Piali. It was his arrival which sparked and inspired the Turkish constant attack on Fort St Elmo, which gave the name of Dragut Point to the spot at Tigne where he mounted his first battery of cannon which wrought havoc amongst the besieged forces in the fort. His devilry and strategy were later seen at their best on Mount Sciberras, where Valletta now stands. That was where on 18th June 1565 he was hit by a ricocheting cannon ball fired from Fort St Angelo. It is historically reported how the other commander Mustapha assumed that Dragut was dead and had his body carried secretly to the tent hospital at Marsa. Although it was known that his corpse was some days later removed from Marsa and taken to Homs in Tripolitania where it was buried, there had always lurked a doubt as to whether he had indeed died after a few days in the hospital as some historians were inclined to believe, or was already dead when he was carried to Marsa. The haunting by his ghost seems to settle this point for history.

Not far from Dragut's imposing mausoleum in Homs where his body was buried there lies a clamp of houses that make a quarter of the village of Tarhuna which for a time was derelict and abandoned as if it was made outcast by the plague. Some speak of the glooms in those houses which threw shadows of fear; others mention the forms of hideous animals ready to spring, or mishapen dwarfs with stubbing arms held high in malediction. What everyone agrees upon is that the quarter was at one time called *Tal-Maltin* (meaning as belonging to the Maltese) and that it was haunted.

The story goes four centuries back when it is said that the quarter in question housed a number of Maltese taken as captives, but who were allowed to live there as a community. This immediately raised a doubt with the knowledge that had withstood the test of time and proof that the corsairs of the Barbary coast in those times ranged with their galleys far and wide all over the Mediterranean descending like eagles on their prey of humanity with which to swell their ransom markets or their ranks of galley slaves. But there seems to have been a different and novel outcome in this particular case. More in the form of a Moslem experiment in having this particular horde of slaves, because they could still be considered as such, living in a restricted freedom to be submitted to pressure aimed at making them deviate from their christian beliefs to that of Islam. That the experiment might initially have failed emanates from what followed when it is reported that the Moslems resorted to taking all the offspring away from their captive parents to have them raised in an Islamic environment. There had already been no love lost between the slaves and their masters, but the abduction of their children touched a sore spot in Maltese character where the strong sense of family was a dominant element then as it is indeed still today. This move took the spark to the powder keg. But what could they do? By now inured to the vicissitudes of their fate they knew there was neither a way of appeal nor any outlet to fight through. What fighting they could put up was translated into an internal stress they could hardly contain which resolved into bitter hate for all that was Moslem, and which was carried right to their death, and continued thereafter with their spirits haunting the malefactors.

This was a case to challenge one's strength in the belief of psychic phenomena, but the facts which originated this story have a page in Maltese history, taking us back to July 1551, when the same Dragut whose ghost still haunts the derelict house in Marsa where he died, had landed on one of his raids with no less than 10,000 men. After finding unexpected resistance he had sailed away to the sister island of Gozo where he practically found no opposition and carried the whole population which was about 6,000 into slavery. This is as far as written history goes; giving no details of the destiny of those captives. It was only through their ghosts haunting houses at Tarhuna that the story was completed. The village still stands in Tripolitania, and there can still be found the community which recognizes its Maltese (or shall we say Gozitan) ancestorship.

Again, ghosts seem to have filled an empty gap in history. But there is here the more important element of the ability of the dead to superimpose their will to haunt with a purpose, which is very often considered unlikely and illogical. Yet, this kind of manifestation is prevalent with ghosts in Malta as I will be showing later, where spirits evidently haunt with a specific purpose to disappear for ever when their scope is attained.

An interesting typical case of our times is that of the Black Knight which haunted Fort Manoel.

This fortress is comparatively modern since it was built by Grandmaster Anthony Manoel de Vilhena between 1723 and 1726. Its ghost is even closer to our times since it materialised during the years immediately after the last war when none other than Captain Eric Brockman from whose writings I obtained the information on the Grey Lady of St Angelo commanded this fortress. It is again to him that I owe the first part of this story, and I could not have found a better source since he was on the spot and at the right time when the Black Knight made his first appearances.

Arrayed in full armour and regalia of the Order of St John, the Knight was persistently seen by both Maltese and English men of the ship's company. Like St Angelo, Fort Manoel was considered as a man-of-war. The ghost had the alarming habit of appearing out of the empty air at several places, but like the Grey Lady he also had his particular spot. In his case it was in the vicinity of a heap of rubble which, before being so reduced by bombs during the war, had been a chapel dedicated by the Grand Master himself to St Anthony of Padua.

When it was resolved to clear the site of rubble in the hope of restoring some sense of order to the chapel, Captain Brockman had set his men to do it. From the moment of their starting work the Black Knight began to appear more frequently, and those who saw him described his attitude as if he was supervising their work. It was during such occasions that the men could take a good look at his face, and descriptions that were given tallied closely to the features of Grand Master Vilhena as they appeared in a portrait by Favray which still hangs in the President's Palace at Valletta. All were now convinced that the ghost of the Grandmaster was personally supervising their work as if he had an interest in what they were doing.

More than for the restoration of the chapel, there was more concern to have some place where church services could be held, and the thought occurred to Captain Brockman that it would be easier to look for a crypt if there happened to be one beneath the chapel and which would probably be intact and ready for use. Indeed there was such a crypt, and it did not take long to obtain the Archbishop's permission to open it. When it was opened it was found out that it had been entered by vandals. The altar was wrecked as were reliefs showing a crucifix and souls in purgatory. The paving stones covering graves were ripped up, exposing human bones that from medallions and inscriptions were identified to have belonged to knights of St John.

The men were set to restore order. The altar was repaired, and the human remains re-buried. In the meantime, the Black Knight continued to supervise, and more than ever before making it evident that he was approving of the men's efforts; perhaps even urging them on. When the crypt was restored, masses were said.

It was then that the Black Knight disappeared, and was never seen again.

It became obvious to all that the scope of the haunting ghost had in the first place been to have the remains of his knights (if he was indeed the Grandmaster) to be re-buried properly and their graves remade with the respect they merited.

I would still not be surprised if even this story, notwithstanding the fact that it is authenticated by the people involved would also be dubbed as a traditional fabrication. However, there is my part to be added for which I can vouch myself.

I have since come to know of two Capuchin monks who during their duties as chaplains to the hospital which was quite close the where the apparitions had occurred, had themselves on different occasions seen the Black Knight. They were not in the least doubtful or surprised since they had already experienced other ghostly manifestations at the 300 year old hospital where they had served. There had been occasions when a brother monk was troubled by cold water he poured into a basin for washing up becoming boiling hot and bubbling. There had also been the occasion when the Medical Superintendent's son was chased by a spectral nun.

But the climax to the Black Knight's episode came only some time ago – when Captain Brockman, now for many years a civilian told me that he was informed that the Black Knight had after all those years of dormancy began haunting again. This time I went myself to Fort Manoel where pitifully enough I found the chapel and its surroundings to be still in the dilapidated state in which they had been left. I was informed that watchmen whose duties made it encumbent on them to be at that place, were avoiding it as hell, because of ghosts. A bigger surprise awaited me however, when I went down into the crypt which the ghost haunted. Vandals had been into it anew – and the graves of the knights were again – open, and with their contents exposed.

Was it this that had brought the Black Knight back?

But this was happening in 1980. There had been much that happened to produce answers to this and other questions like it, during a gap of thirty five years. A gap that revolutionized Malta, her history – and also her ghosts.

Chapter 2
Palaces, a Castle and a Proof

Ghosts are as old as man. They have come down through the centuries misted in legand, shrouded with dark dread, and more often than not reflecting the past and characteristics of the nation they haunt.

It is very likely that those who at some time or other have had encounters with ghosts and the inexplicable that surrounds them cannot but believe in such psychic phenomena. This is the term which describes the various manifestations which do not always conform to the laws of terrestrial life. Such encounters make believers and also the sceptics. It has been like this since the first known times of civilisation in Malta – and this is saying something since it is known that there was such a civilisation in the Maltese Archipelago thousands of years before England emerged from the Ice Age. One could have hopefully expected that as the numbers of believers would get bigger it would bring nearer the day when man would learn more about the undiscovered laws which may throw more light on the illogical and chaotic that still prevails in the world of ghosts. There is however no such expectation in sight, and this may be because of the cardinal law that has been constantly evident and proven that not everyone possesses the ability to see them.

Some attribute this to the faculty of Extra Sensory

Perception (ESP) which enables certain persons to sense that is denied to others. So much so that many a time this faculty is called the Sixth Sense. It is presumed that some ability akin to this may be what makes a person able to see a ghost when another does not. It could be better described as one's aptitude to tune on to the wavelength used by ghostly transmissions. Because we can speak of transmission and reception in the case of ghostly manifestions. All this is evidenced by the many who can see ghosts while others can't, even though they might hear them. There are also those who can "smell" ghosts. The smelling is in this case an allegory to the ability of sensing the presence of ghostly influences.

The Maltese have also found their own description to explain this by referring to those who can see ghosts as having *Għajnejn li jaraw* which means "seeing eyes." The rest are aptly confined to the class of the unseeing, where many sceptics can still be found.

It is a fact that the Maltese are a believing people. Their Faith is full of mysterious dogmas which they implicitly believe even though they are only hazily perceptive of their meaning. By nature too, they crave for the mysterious. Why should there therefore be so many sceptics?

The answer incredibly is that Malta does not know the truth behind its abundant psychic phenomena. This is because of the simple reason that those who are susceptible to it tend to keep it to themselves; not only because they fear ridicule from non-believers, but also of the sense of awe and apprehension that ghostly manifestations carry with them. There are occasions when some exceptional haunting occurs in public and cannot escape publicity; yet, even here, mouths clamp shut and eyes are averted with the result that it reaches interested ears in such a hazy way that it is often aborted before taking form of reality.

I was sceptical once because I just did not believe in ghosts. There could therefore not be any sense of awe or apprehension in my case. But I was then hearing so many sinister stories as the ones already recounted, to which I listened, even with some avidity. It occurred to me that had there been any truth in them, it was not helped to flourish by the tendency of the British to languish in this branch of the occult and taking things for granted during their 164 years of occupation. Indeed, now I believe that as they had discouraged other Maltese initiatives they must have also killed some colourful ghosts in Malta. The few stories that came out were soon forgoten, as very often happens with the dirty jokes one hears. Yet, stories of ghosts kept coming, not only revealing a hidden past but also blending it with the occult activity of the present to make any reasonable person aware of what could be the fantastic truth behind apparitions, noises, poltergeists and similar manifestations that make the ghosts of Malta. One has only to go four centuries back, which times are still brightly reflected to-day in edifices, architecture, living memories – and also in ghosts.

The Palace of the Grand Masters in Valletta built by the French Grand Master Jean l'Eveque de la Cassiere who ruled between 1572 and 1586 had through the time of British occupation always been one of the three official residences of the British Governor. Entering it from Valletta's main square is like walking to a backdrop in history. Its setting and architecture echoes the high times of wealth and prosperity, and takes one through the mirror of time into an older concealed world. It had originally been the home of Grand Masters of the Order of St John, whose armoury is still preserved. That the palace was maintained through centuries to keep abreast with times till this very day is reflected by the House of Representatives which is housed in there. It had throughout all this time, but particularly during British rule, become the Mecca of various high dignatories, and it had even welcomed royalty. Its inimitable Chapter Halls were the venue of pagaentry and State Balls always resplendent with the brilliance of a vanishing empire. Its story in quiet moments makes one think of a romantic and lovely old woman, full of peace and memories. But all this could have never been complete without a ghost. The British never mentioned any. The Maltese may not forgive me for foisting such a story on this public building. However, the palace is said to have harboured an elusive ghost.

It had to be an English lady who stayed in this palace

to tell me of the days when she was constantly annoyed by its ghosts. Because she believed there were more than one. It appears that there was a particular room where she often heard a commotion like that caused by cats and dogs when fighting. But on going into the room to investigate she would find nothing and the noise would cease. Only to start again as soon as she leaves the room. At this juncture of time there was another female relative living in the palace to whom this gracious lady always paid the compliment of bidding good night before retiring, even if she happened to return late. On one occasion when she went in for the usual salutation she found her in bed and asleep. So she was going out again not wishing to wake her. But her relative called her, because she was far from being asleep. She was indeed terrorized, she told her, by somebody who had been in that room a while before. It was someone she couldn't see, but none the less felt him or her close to her bed.

There was however one occasion when the ghost manifested itself. It was in the form of a big cat which had certainly no reason to be there. When the lady who told me all this had gone after it to investigate, the cat jumped out of a window to drop in a yard where there were some men at work. But when she asked them where the cat had gone after failing to see it, they replied that they had seen no cat falling from the window.

No explanation was ever given for these happenings, and although the lady in question vouches for them, she never learned any details of the story behind them. So she could not make any guess regarding the nature of her visitants. It was a pity, really, because when the story came out it could only arouse one's curiosity, and nothing else.

Grand Master de la Cassiere was in 1581 succeeded by another French, Hugues Lourbenx de Verdalle who left for posterity the imposing structure of Verdala Castle which was later to be closely connected with the story of the Blue Lady.

This story had been rife for ages but at the time of which I am writing was dying out on lack of popular proof, and was indeed already downgraded to the ranks of legend. The castle however, which is better measured in distance by the pleasant walk along beautiful countryside from the town of Rabat, than by kilometres, has a fascinating story. Built in 1585 it was, as it is still to-day conspicuous by its vast square form, challenging in site, martial and feudal in aspect. Its thick walls rise loftly from the moat to the battlemented towers belying the description of a country retreat as its motto *Cedant curae loco* – "let cares surrender to the place," suggests it to have been.

Truly enough one couldn't think of a better summer resort being as it is at such a prominent spot with a bird's eye view of all Malta and a part of Gozo, with the blue sea on every side. Around the castle then there lie spread out the only wood-like gardens of the island – Boschetto Gardens, with their numerous trees, orchards and orange groves, as if to emulate their lofty master and offer respite to all from heat and sun. These gardens are seen at their best on the occasion of the feast of St Peter and St Paul on 29 June popularly called *Mnarja* which is a corruption of *Luminaria* intended to refer to the illuminated churches of Rabat on that day. The gardens are still on this feast the venue for an agricultural show with horse races and fatstock contests, and crowds of people spend most of the night there eating the traditional stewed rabbit which is washed down with gallons of wine.

But if Verdala Castle belies its scope in form, it had attained it in use since it has always been used as a summer residence by the rulers of Malta. Hence it had become the second official residence of the Governor. It was only recently that it was transformed into a residence for VIP's visiting the island.

The Blue Lady was supposed to be a young woman, a niece of Grand Master De Rohan, an unwillingly chosen light o'love. Rather than heeding her objections and letting her go, her rejected suitor kept her imprisoned in her room until one day she managed to get to a window through which she fell to her death. The legend goes that she began to haunt the castle, appearing in the blue dress she had on at the point of her death.

The story might have ended there with the ghost

being forgotten in the legendary fables of local folk-lore. Indeed all relative writings and everyone in Malta do not go any further. However, it is a fact that during the time when Field Marshal Lord Methuen was Governor of Malta between 1915 and 1919 he had a guest staying with him at Verdala Castle. It was some British Foreign Office official – a Mr Howard-Jones, who one day asked him who was the woman in blue whose reflection he often saw in the mirror when he was dressing.

The secret was out, and there was no need for the governor's explanation since there were many of the staff who had seen her.

Legend is transmitted by hearsay. But I had this story from a person who was present at Verdala Castle on that day the secret broke out. Indeed the description sometimes given of the room where the Blue Lady was said to appear, tallies exactly with the room where Mr Howard-Jones stayed.

It suddenly began to seem to me that as I delved into the mysteries of Malta's past I was unearthing material which could one day lead me to the proof that mattered. As I was sceptical I was not taking everything I heard for granted. I was listening to everyone but using only first hand information given by persons who were personally involved for further investigation. When because of the lapse of time or lack of evidence this became impossible my efforts might have seemed to be perfunctory, but they were not. Every bit of information I obtained was being somehow reserved to be tried to fit into the big mosaic that I was already thinking of building up. Without knowing why, I began investigating something in which I did not believe. There were many easier things to do than investigating ghosts. Less painstaking too. But here as well I felt they would be less rewarding when I considered the vast history that stood to be given the tag of authenticity, and what this could mean for Malta and the knowledge about the occult. But it never escaped my feeling that there had to be the irrevocable and unchallenging proof which would produce the fundamental facts behind ghostly manifestations. I knew this was going to be difficult since I could not see ghosts. But I also felt that I would some day make it.

I didn't know then how close I was to it. In the meantime there was another story to come.

Three grandmasters and twenty eight years after de Verdalle there was another Frenchman elected Grand Master – Antoine de Paule, who was to rule from 1623 to 1635. It was him who made up the beautiful gardens of San Anton and built the adjoining palace. There is little to say on the gardens, with their flower terraces and orange groves all set into parallel fragments separated by walls covered by multi coloured Bougainvillaea. They were to delight Sir Walter Scott in 1831, as they still attract Maltese and foreigners to-day. But the palace is something different. It is a rambling and delightful country house swarming in beautifully laid out gardens. It reflects very well the reputation of its builder for soft living and luxury, which he had introduced in the Order. But if indeed this had been the purpose behind the palace it was quickly emulated by his followers – not only those of the Order, but also the British who made of San Anton Palace the third official residence of the governor. It became his house of habitation, leaving the Palace of the Grandmasters in Valletta for administrative and ceremonial functions, and Verdala Castle as his summer house. Again, British and Maltese diarchies, since it is now being used as Presidential residence, had inherited a magnificent patrimonial house located in one of the island's quietest and unspoiled spots.

Looking at it from the garden, alone, on a windless day, with gorgeous flowers at your feet, and the rest of the flower beds flung out behind you in many coloured tapestry of light and shade, the palace presents a spectacular sight of brittling Malta stone against a clear blue sky. No sound is likely to mar the haunting silence. Except the singing birds. The only other sounds are the whispers of history. Again, one might reasonably expect it to have a ghost. it is said it had one. Not the ghost of some knight or damsel one would have expected of its romantic setting. But it was haunted by a Moor.

This was also during the time when Lord Methuen was Governor. There were at the time two sisters living in that palace, one of whom was constantly seeing this

Moor in her dreams and telling her that he would bring rivalry and jealousy between her and her sister. But there was no actual manifestation notwithstanding the fact that both sisters sensed his presence everywhere. One evening however, anticipating the usual invasion by mosquitoes which tend to converge from Hibiscus trees when it is warm, one of the sisters was fixing a mosquito net at her window.

"Suddenly," she told me, "as I put my hand out of the window, something hit me on the wrist. it was a numbing blow. There was nothing outside, and there could not have been anyone since the window was on the first floor. I knew it must have been the ghost behind that blow."

It might have been a poor sort of manifestation. But some time later there was the Bishop of London staying as a guest in the palace. To Lord Methuen's consternation who was a sticker for time the Bishop failed to turn up at the appointed hour for a ceremonial dinner being held in his honour. When he went down half an hour late, he apologized to Lord Methuen.

"Your Excellency," he said, "I must apologize for this delay. But for the last half an hour I was detained in my room."

The Governor looked at him without a word. But his attitude implied the obvious question.

"It was supernatural trouble I had," said the Bishop, "and I had to carry out an exorcism before I could leave my room."

Then he explained how the door of his room had opened by itself when he came to leave and was then shut in his face preventing him from going out. Thrice it opened and shut again by itself giving him no chance to leave the room. It was only when he recited the prayers of exorcism that what spirit was at that door had relented.

In the same way as Antoine de Paule had left his memory green among the many who still enjoy his beautiful garden, and built San Anton Palace for the rulers of posterity, he had also in his time started a residential area. As fate would have it there was in it the one particular house which was to play an important part in my transmutation into the world of ghosts.

The house in question is in Paola, now a modern town to which the Maltese name of *Raħal Ġdid* meaning the "New Village" has stuck. There is little to remind one that this place was ever a village as it might have been when it took its name from the Grandmaster who built it. The trees and rubble walls are gone. So are the fields and the men that tilled them. One would go long distances now before he would find a building reflecting those first days of origin. Instead, there are modern buildings, good roads, markets, playing fields, shopping centres and of course a majestic church which is one of the biggest in Malta.

The protagonist house is a normal infinitely pleasing building, as it still looks to this very day. But its comparatively youthful exterior when I knew it was belied the moment one crossed the threshold. Whatever beauty was still to be found inside was the result of care and taste by the tenants. However, it holds very sweet memories to me since it was there I met Adeline, one of the daughters of those tenants, who is now my wife. Besides the parents and Adeline there was then one other daughter Carmelina living there, as well as five brothers – John, Frank, George, William and Maurice. I mention them by name since they will all feature in the dramatic events that will follow. Four other sons and another daughter who were all married lived on their own. There was also living in the house a grandmother who had her rooms on the second floor.

As I had occasion to learn later there had already been various strange manifestations by the time I became a regular visitor to the house in 1945. Emmanuela, the mother, used to hear bronchitic breathing in her bedroom, and the sound of footsteps going up or descending stairs. There was also the sound of breaking crockery in the dining room to be heard during the night when everyone was upstairs which was very often quickly investigated by the boys who would rush down only to find everything in order and untouched. But a strong and discreet silence was maintained in those first days, and none of them was willing to draw me on the subject of the haunting since all of them knew that I would not believe them, having already expressed my scepticism on the subject of ghosts.

One evening however, there was a new development. While all the members of the family were sitting round the table in the dining room saying their prayers as they always did, Carmelina gave a scream and startled everyone out of his wits. When she was asked what had happened she told them between frantic sobbing how on looking at the mirror over a sideboard in front of her she saw the reflection of a man who was standing behind her. She described him as being a youngish dark complexioned man, wearing a thin moustache and looking more like a South American from the hat he wore to his braided waistcoat and shirt. No one else saw him; not even those who like her were looking at the mirror. But on the following day I could easily see that she was still suffering from shock, and the attitude of the rest was one of depression and fear. it was evident to me that something was the matter, and obviously I asked about it. It was then that all their caution was put aside and I was told everything.

I did not express myself in my usual boisterous way to poke fun at them seeing how all of them were affected. But I still did not believe them, since they were saying things which had happened and gone and could never be verified. It was only a few days later that things began to happen again to hint that something abnormal might have been going on in that house.

I had arrived earlier than usual, and Adeline was away at her sewing classes. So I waited for her. At 4 p.m. there was her grandmother returning from church, on the dot, and as usual welcomed me from the entrance hall without entering the dining room where I was. Then as was her drill she continued on her way upstairs. After a while she came down again to pick up something.

"Where is Adeline?" she asked me.

"She hasn't come back yet," I said.

"But she was here when I came in a while ago."

"No," I said, "I was alone when you came in, just as I am now."

"But I saw her," she said emphatically. "She was dressed in red, and she had her arm around you."

To a believer in ghosts this might have meant that besides Adeline there was another girl who fancied me in that house. But I certainly had not felt anything to indicate this. Neither bodily nor emotionally. So I dismissed the whole thing as imagination on the part of the old woman.

A few days later however, when I had also arrived early and again found Adeline away, the grandmother had strangely enough returned from church earlier than usual. It wasn't much; only ten minutes I thought as I looked at my watch. When I looked up again intending to remark about it the old woman was already going upstairs. It was strange for her to return early; but stranger still was the way how she had refrained from the usual greeting. I was still wondering at this strange behaviour when at 4 p.m. the door opened, and again there was grandmother coming in as if she had only just returned from church. I was flabbergasted. When she welcomed me I asked her before she could go upstairs.

"Tell me," I told her, "didn't you come in ten minutes ago?"

"No," she said.

"Then who was that other woman who came in?" I asked again.

She replied that she didn't know what I was talking about. It was odd, but the old woman only seemed amused at my astonishment. I had distinctly seen her coming in and there was no possibility of any mistake. I did not say anything to anyone then being occupied with trying to explain that occurrence rationally to myself, but my mind was continually flashing the question as to whether after all the house was really haunted. On the other hand when I found myself thinking again of what had alternately seemed an unghostlike activity I found myself at a loss to find sufficient evidence to point at any solution of that mysterious occurrence. I had become so much occupied that I was already lending myself to compromise by putting what had happened out of mind when I realized with a newly found wave of excitement, followed by as sudden a rush of self comtempt – that this could launch me into looking for the proof I instinctively always felt I wanted.

As I kept my silence, now, I could not help lending a

more ready ear to the stories about the various manifestations that I was being told were going on in that house. Everyone seemed to be hearing things except me. There was my fiancee too who did not seem to have been sharing the manifestations. In her case there was only a recurring dream of an angry woman whom she could describe perfectly to me, telling her that she would kill her. As the weeks rolled on, I tried to put questions in the way of feelers to start conversations with the purpose of trying to go into the past of the house, but I drew only blank replies making of my half hearted attempts a series of losing battles. It had been obvious, however, that whatever was going on was a product of not more than a century back. This would be a clear indication, if proved to be authentic, of the continued supernatural influences throughout time. I was on the verge of calling the whole thing off when one day a neighbour called to say that whenever he went past the house on his way to work in the early morning while it was still dark he was often seeing all the lights on as for some special occasion. Coming from an outsider when it was known that all the family had refrained from speaking of such matters outside the house, this had weakened my decision to return back to my old scepticism.

It was at that time that the eldest son of the family had returned from Alexandria where he had been serving, and with him came his wife who was a Suez born Maltese he married there. Arrangements were made for them to be given temporary accommodation in the same house until they would find a place of their own. But on their first night there, as they were going upstairs, the wife gave a scream and the next moment came tumbling down the stairs bruising herself and fracturing an arm. When asked, she said that at the top of the first flight of stairs where they joined a landing she was suddenly confronted by a woman all dressed in black, wearing a tall pointed headgear from which dropped a black veil over her eyes. She had appeared from nowhere, and barred her way. Then she had pushed her.

This was an unexpected *contratemps*. If there had really been this manifestation, and I had no reason to disbelieve it, I thought that this woman in black could not have been the poltergeist behind the not so malevolent nightly manifestations in the dining room, if she had made her debut with violence. But if the ghost was seen it might be possible to identify her, I thought with my first shiver. This could perhaps lead me to the proof I wanted. But the more I thought I began to find it harder to settle for or against what was to be done. I was incapable of concentration realising I was now a man with a problem. I knew – and I was angry with myself because I knew – that I was eking out my resistance to the existence of ghosts. But there had been too many ifs in my arguments. I became nigh helpless. Yet I knew I had to do something. With the ghostly manifestations now being more or less concentrated in one particular room, this was emptied and avoided. Bedding was taken to another room so that all could be together. It must have been the desperation more than stupidity when I asked to be allowed to spend one night in the haunted room.

At first they wouldn't hear of it, but when I persisted, even with my spirit struggling with the unreasonable and dreadful whim, it was agreed that I should do it. Only thus I could resolve the problem that was burdening me.

Although I didn't know it then, another person with whom I was to become acquainted later was having a very similar problem. Michael Spiteri had never believed in ghosts. Not even when his policeman father showed him the big stately house at Msida seafront which happened to be on his beat and had many a time to be investigated after he would hear noises of merchandise being moved inside at an hour when no one was expected to be there. On every occasion, everything would be found in its place. It was because of the haunting that the place was used as a warehouse.

Michael had been married for some time and living with his mother-in-law. His prayers for a house of his own were finally answered and in a still devastated Malta where places of habitation were hard to come by he found a flat in a newly reconstructed block in Gżira. It was just the place where with his wife and young daughter he could start life on his own. All would have been well had it not been for the unexplained noises which would start at midnight coming as he thought from the walls of one particular room. By nature a patient and easygoing man Michael did not jump to any conclusions and tried to find out where the noises were coming from and what was causing them. But there was nothing and no one who could possibly have been making them. When for the umpteenth time he tried to pinpoint the exact spot of disturbance it seemed to vary until he reached the conclusion that the noises were coming from nowhere. But he was sure they were still there, as was also his wife even though she did not raise the point with him. However, she began asking her mother to stay with them more often as a resort to some added protection and companionship.

Both Michael and his wife seemed to be refraining from encroaching on each other's feelings about the noises maybe through fear of causing any worry to each other or the ridicule that any precipitation of a simple noise into the realism of a ghostly manifestation could bring. Whatever it was, both of them were hoping that the noises would stop. But if they did not talk, the mother-in-law did. Not plainly as one would have expected, but in hidden warnings full of inuendos, hinting at changing residence which Michael did not want, and preferred bearing with the ordeal a little longer. In the meantime the noises continued.

The spouses might have carried on in their mutual self imposed ignorance of the implied situation had it not been for their child. She began screaming one night when she said she saw two mice in her night pot.

Both parents found relief in the common assumption of a childish dream. But when there was a recurrance, this time with the same mice being in a water basin they could not persist in their attitude when both of them saw the mice. They were not the usual rodents all too willing to scurry away to any disturbance but they were there sniffing at all and everything as if it were their nature to do so. Even though, close to them there was also a cat. A big spectral cat.

This time horror seized the wife, an undescribable and undefinable horror – an overwhelming certainty of supreme and accomplished calamity, which infected everyone and remained with them throughout the night.

When it was dawn Michael went over to the Parish Priest and told him everything. That same day the pious priest went to the flat and blessed the place, sprinkling the holy water and reciting prayers. The night was peaceful. And so were many others after it. The days that followed gave the family a welcome respite. To Michael more time to think and fathom why and how ghosts should manifest as mice and a cat. He had heard stories of such incongruent apparitions but it was only now that he believed them, when he had seen them himself. Besides the enigma of why should a ghost or ghosts take such form there was the other more important axiom he had heard and believed that ghosts never haunt a new building since theirs is a sort of personality which remains after death imposed on place or spot where death had occurred. His flat was a new building and he had been the first tenant to go into it.

His feelings remained a problem until he began to hear the noises again. This time he went back to the Parish Priest, and was advised to leave that flat. When Michael mentioned his two enigmas, the priest told him that the ghosts were those of damned souls, who had probably died in sin there.

"But how could it be father?" asked Michael, "if I was the first one to come into this new place?"

"Oh yes, it could," replied the priest.

Then he told him how the block where his flat was, had only been a reconstruction of another block which had been heavily damaged by air attacks during the war, and was not what one could call new.

Michael understood the priest's words to imply that there might have been some influence still prevailing from the previous building which remained with the extension which was his place. If there had been some emotional death in that previous building of which he did not know . . .

But he was not allowed to think any further when somebody else who knew of the incident, said to him: "I knew the previous building very well Michael. In fact when it was almost demolished by bombs, I was with the Air Raid Precautions people who came over to render help to anyone who might have been trapped underneath the debris."

"And were there any?" asked Michael excitedly, thinking that this might provide a clue to his enigma.

"Yes," said his informer with a knowing light in his eyes. "There were three. Two sailors and a prostitute, caught and killed in the state and posture of their vile act."

It was hard for Michael to think of two men and one woman symbolized by two mice and a cat. But it seemed to him that his problems were solved.

I wasn't as lucky with mine. I had hoped to get so much from my night vigil in the haunted room, and grew so excited when the occasion came. My whim was well intentioned although prompted by the state of tension that had gripped me. When I went to the house on the appointed night I had thought of some weapon that I could take with me, as if ghosts could be subdued with weapons. And I finished by taking a crucifix and a loaded revolver. This latter was indicative that I was still allowing the possibility of meeting some earthly being rather than a ghost. As matters turned out I saw and heard nothing that night, and there could not have been a more disappointed person on the following morning.

It was an outcome which might have made any other person in my position reverse his changing views. But it did nothing of the sort to me. Instead I found myself apt to compassionate the familiars' condition in that they were also disappointed in my being unable to confirm and believe their situation, and I began to be more attentive to their stories. It was the least I could do. The circumstance which was to convince me of the hauntings arrived quicker than I had expected, however, when someone was found who was willing to take over their house in exchange for his. Honestly I might have even been sorry to have that house going to someone else which would definitely stop any further possibility to investigate the ghosts. Because that was what I was doing amounted to. But on the other hand there was the condition of the family to be considered. Somehow, I felt I had to make it a point to be present when the interested tenant came to see the house.

She was a woman. But what struck me immediately

as important was that she brought her dog with her. I knew that it was said that dogs possess a very high extra sensory perception, and can smell a ghost when a human doesn't. I realised that the animal could provide me with the wanted proof.

The woman came through the door pulling her dog on a leash, and while all those present were showering attentions on her, I had eyes only for the dog. They made a few steps, and nothing happened. Then suddenly the dog stopped, and would not go a step further. It began growling and howling. When its mistress bent down to pet it, it crouched and whined with obvious abject fear.

Dogs do neither lie nor hide their feelings, and I immediately knew what that animal was going through. I found in that canine attitude the right conviction that ghosts did exist, and what's more, that some of them were indeed haunting that house. My conviction must have also been shared by the woman who until a short while back had been so keen to exchange residence. Now she suddenly changed her mind, and as she turned back to go out, the dog ran before her dragging her in its wake as if relieved to have broken the spell that throughout all this time had drawn its eyes in a hypnotic stare at the top of the stairs where the brother's wife had been pushed by the spectral woman in black some time before.

Chapter 3

Haunted Houses – a Debacle for Conviction

One enormous piece of evidence for the existence of ghosts in Malta has always been found in the substantial number of beautiful houses that had remained unoccupied throughout the years. Particularly during those following immediately after the end of the last war when Malta was passing through a crisis brought about by housing shortage. It was a common saying that the unoccupied houses were all haunted. But none would say this in a way that it might reach the landlord's ears for fear of being forced with a lawsuit for defamation of the building.

Indeed, this stigma was to become public knowledge in the time that was to come later with the building boom in the sixties when there was the exodus from Britain with thousands of Britishers making a bee-line for Malta attracted by prospects of a quiet retirement in the sun with an income-tax of sixpence in the pound. That mass migration has since found a place in local history and remained conspicuous by the impact made by the tendency of the immigrants to bring with them their fancy prices which were cheap by their standards but ridiculously high for the local scene. None would blame the Maltese for playing up – and God bless them, they did, bringing unexpected and much wanted money into the country but also spoiling the stability of prices, which has since never recovered. As if those were not enough, there followed the enterpreneurs, all intent to share in the obvious wealth their own people had prospected. They came complete with their dubious knowhow and bags of money to spend on every derelict piece of land or house they could lay their hands upon. When they dug up human skulls in the soil they called it Atlantis, and old pottery spelt Carthage. The Maltese giggled at their discoveries and increased their prices. In this way chunks of Malta were destined to change hands for easy cash. Every conceivable bit of land or building found its ready buyer.

Except the derelict haunted houses. They remained vacant and abandoned, some of them till this very day. But none could have known this in those first days of 1947.

I was convinced then that the stately house pitifully being used as a store and workshop on the seafront at Msida overlooking the picturesque creek lined with yachts from the nearby Yacht Marina was haunted. But this was not because of what I heard about it. It was neither its forlorn look and spooky aspect that were present through my thoughts. In my mind there was only the imprinted reflection of what I had seen in the house at Paola. The meaning of what I knew to have been there, culminating in the dog's reactions seemed held in a single picture which was to remain with me forever. When I learned that this was the same building that had instigated police investigations, when constables on patrol (amongst them Michael Spiteri's father) had regularly heard noises of merchandise being moved behind closed doors at night, I could not help making comparisons. As if to weigh on deliberations being made there was the case of the men working in this house who could take no more of the manifestations, and left, never to return to it again. It was then that I had the premonition that what I had been through was not complete, and much less conclusive. Maybe this was what renewed by anxiety to know more.

As if to tone down the spooky atmosphere but certainly to bring in a different element of the handicap Malta was labouring under because of her ghosts and the people's mentality, there was close to the house at

Msida another big place, not less stately and prominent in look. It is still there to-day. It was once used as residence by Lord Nelson during his brief stay in Malta when he came over to push the French out in October 1798. It was Nelson too who had recommended this house to his friend, the distinguished scholar John Hookham Frere who occupied it after his retirement from the British diplomatic service. It was in it too that Hookham Frere hosted his other close friend, Sir Walter Scott during his stay on the island. Strangely enough, these premises which became government property by expropriation when a part of their vast garden was taken to provide a site for the Nursing School of St Luke's Hospital, were not given the attention they merited. The magnificent set up is being lost in misuse. As are also the remains of the garden containing the spring which the Maltese architect and engineer Grognet de Vasse' had in the theory he propounded about Malta having been part of Atlantis, alluded to it as being an outlet of the river Styx of the sunken continent. Nobody has ever felt the urge to crusade about a building; but it is here apparent that legendary and historical heritage is being suppressed. The only reason that occurred to me for mentioning it is that the house could be haunted. It was indeed. Not by any violent manifestation. But the sound of a drum being beaten was at one time heard in it. Then, in a particular room once a year before Christmas there is the strong smell of sweet and confectionery.

The stories of two particular houses in Valletta have remained on Maltese lips till this very day. They are recounted everytime converation turns to Maltese ghosts as if becoming standing examples of the interesting local phenomena. One of the houses was in that part of St Ursola Street where steps take one down its steep incline – so steep that a big house like the one in question could lose a whole floor in its own length. Those who remember the house in the first years of the last war describe it as a building which in its initial days of the seventeenth century must have been very imposing. But then, with its faded yellow stucco all dirty and the plaster flaking off it radiated a sense of dereliction. Indeed, it had then already been empty for a good many years. The last persons who were known to have gone into the place had been two English naval officers.

Their advenure had begun with a chance encounter during the night with a lady of their time. Wearing black silk of the period, with an abundance of embroidered lace she might have given them the wrong impression when she accosted them near Citygate (in those days called Porta Reale) at the entrance to the city, had it not been for her *faldetta* which covered her head and most of her person. That's why it was worn by respectable women. Even so, whatever doubts there could have been were dispelled when the lady spoke. Hers was the voice of a cultured woman.

From what she said the two young officers gathered that she was asking for their help since she had locked herself out of her house. Would they help her to get in? Her house was in St Ursola Street.

It was indeed strange why she should have picked a couple of complete foreigners to do such a thing for her. There were Maltese men about, and the police station could not have been very far away. But after all the night was theirs, and their way to the Customs House and the *dgħajsas* which plied to their ships lay through that street and past her house. So they accompanied her willingly.

St Ursola Street looked dark and foreboding at that time of night. The lights on the walls were evenly and far spaced, and just adequate to keep a man from breaking his leg. There was no other soul to be seen, and as they walked down the stone steps made sway-backed by centuries of clattering feet, their sound in unison reverbrated to the gable ends of houses, reaching high, cutting the night sky into a sliver.

The woman had not spoken a word since they had left. Now that they knew they must have been close to where she was taking them, there was no will for conversation. Both of them were soon looking around as if seeing the place for the first time. At the closed doors, and shuttered windows above and around, with no trace of sound coming from behind their closed shutters. And as always, there came to fan their faces, the night breeze that funnelled up this street from the sea.

When they reached the house, there was little or no difficulty for one of the officers to get to a window with the help of his friend, and with a pocket-knife spring the latch of the window shutters. The rest was relatively easier. He scrambled inside, and aided by the moonlight which now flooded the room he was in, from the open window, he found candles to light. In the light of five candles in a silver candelabra he had his first surprise on finding himself in a magnificently furnished room. His immediate impression was that he had entered a house of the well-to-do. Then taking up the candelabra he descended a wide staircase to the ground floor. With every step he walked he could not fail to notice the wealth in paintings, curtains and other rich embellishments that covered the walls. The reflection of the candles from the marble floor was sprinkling the crystal that was all round him with a thousand pin-points of light.

When he reached the main door, there was the key on the inside. This should have set him thinking. There was in those days no yale keys or the like enabling one to lock a door by just pulling it shut. It was unlikely for one to lock that kind of door from the outside and leave the key inside. But his did not occur to him. So he opened the door, and let the lady and his friend in.

If the house had impressed him in the light of the candelabra, it struck both of them dumb with astonishment when more lights were put on. Its magnificence was now also enhanced with the lady joining them, divested of her faldetta, and showing her shining black hair which did justice to her beautiful face now covered with a charming smile. She asked them to sit down, and served drinks in goblets of cut glass. The two Englishmen could not help conclude, with that splendour around them and the company of its lovely mistress, that their time had not been wasted.

One of them asked if he might smoke and the lady nodded her consent.

After more conversation and a second drink it was time to leave. There was a simple farewell, and they left. It was then, while on their way to the ship that questions began to assail them. How could such a household be devoid of any servants or relatives? And with the key still in its place from the inside how could the lovely lady have locked herself out? There was also the question of her identity. How could she have done so much without telling them who she was? Too many questions, but no answers. It was as if it had all been a dream. But it wasn't. They had been awake and alert to what was going on as they were still aware then. As if to prove the point to himself one of them decided to have a smoke.

It was then he realised that he had left his silver cigarette case in the house.

It might have been a stratagem to bring a second call which the lady had certainly not hinted at. But it wasn't. It had been all a simple genuine moment of forgetfulness. Whatever it was he was not leaving that cigarette case there. So they decided to call for it on the morrow.

When they made their way to the place on the following day they received their first shock. The house was there all right, but the facade that now confronted them in the daylight was out of context with what they knew to be on the inside. They could see the plaster all flaked off and the stone that had been beneath it being all black and dirty with time and neglect. The door, devoid of any colour was firmly shut, giving the impression that it had not been opened for many years, and the balconies looked like shapeless wooden contraptions about to fall at the first touch. Could they have made a mistake? But no. It was the same house all right. Even the shutter they had forced open the previous night was still ajar.

For a moment or two they stood still, not knowing what to do. Then one of them walked to the door and pulled the rusty bellpull hanging there by a heavy chain. There was no response save a protesting squeal. A second pull then parted the corroded contraption.

There were a couple of passers by, looking strangely at them. It was not difficult to know what they were thinking of the two crazy Englishmen trying to resurrect a dead house. Because by now there was no doubt of this. However, there was now more than a retrieval of a cigarette case involved. The situation as things had happened seemed to offer them a challenge. And this made them act.

Throwing all caution to the wind they repeated their act of the previous night. One of them made a quick entry through the open window. This time he dropped into a bare and empty room. In the absence of candles and candelabra he used his matches to find his way about. The staircase to the ground floor was there as he had left it; but now it was stone cold bare. When he reached the door and managed to open it, his friend joined him. Then they explored the creepy house together. It was deserted; but what was obvious to them was that it had been in that derelict state for many years.

There was a flash of a second thought that they might have after all dreamed or somehow imagined all that had happened. But no. They found the room where they had been entertained the night before – now all covered with dust and cobwebs. But to decide it all for them there was something which brittled as they struck a match. Yes, it was the cigarette case, lying just where it had been left.

As if this was not enough proof of their mysterious adventure of the night before there were still visible in the dust on the floor their two sets of footprints which they recognised as having been their own. But there was no indication whatsoever of any footprints that should have been there as belonging to the woman who had been with them.

They had no doubt now that on the previous night they had been entertained by a ghost.

The story of the other house is somewhat similar and having particularly the same twist. It was recounted by Lord Lorne and published in the *Blackwood Magazine* in 1887. In this case the house is not being identified because it still stands to-day.

Lord Lorne recounted how a friend of his who had his office in Valletta was one night returning home on foot, when near a small cemetery which lay half way to his town of residence was accosted by two women dressed all in black who walked out of the cemetery. They asked him to accompany them home to Valletta. It wasn't an enjoyable proposition, but either through pity or curiosity, he agreed to walk back with them. Maybe he was afraid.

When they reached Valletta, however, curiosity took the better of him and rather than leaving he accompanied them wherever they went. Judging by the way they roamed all over the place he was convinced they knew the city well.

Finally they stopped in front of a house, and without saying a word they indicated their wish to have him go with them. And he did. It occurred to him that they hadn't spoken a word after their invitation to accompany them. It began also to dawn on him now that he did not see them using any key to open the door. He began to believe that it was not a normal situation he had launched himself in. But what musings he began having were soon dispelled when he saw the beautiful entrance hall in which he was ushered. There were statues all round and a wonderful variation of decoration plants. In an adjoining yard he could also see orange trees full of ripe fruit. At the back of the hall there was a marble staircase which could be reached through an arched door. Over the arch there was an inscription on marble – *Omni Somnia*, the meaning of which he did not know.

When the two women went up the stairs he followed them until they reached a small room on the second floor. For a moment he expected to be offered a drink or a coffee, and tried to prompt it by asking whether he could smoke a cigar. Assent was nodded, and again there was not a word uttered. Maybe this was too much for him. If they were not being so communicative he could at least learn who they were. It might even make them talk. So he did ask them for their name. One of them answered and told him that her name was Bismilla. It was a strange name, but the voice in which she said it was stranger. It was not what one would call a natural human voice, but more like a faint shout from a distance. There was nothing else for him to do in that place and making his excuses he left.

It was on the following day that he discovered he had left his cigar case in that house. Not wishing to have a noisome experience repeated he sent a messenger from his club to get it for him. But to his amazement the messenger returned to say he could not find any house the way he described it. He sent him again once more only to get the same result. So he decided to go himself.

He found the house all right, but it was in a much different state from the previous night. There were dilapidated walls, and cobwebs covered all apertures. He could not understand what was going on. So he asked a shoemaker who had his shop in the vicinity who lived in that house.

"No one has lived in that house for the last hundred years," said the shoemaker, "it is reputed to be haunted by two sisters who had last lived there."

The reply was not pleasant, but it fitted all that he had been through. Rather than diminishing his interest, however, it made him bolder. After all, there was still his cigar case he wanted to retrieve. So he asked the shoemaker from where he could get the keys of the house. It was a nun who had them, and it wasn't easy to get her to give them to him. But finally she did. When he entered the house the hall was anything but what it had been in his first visit. The statues lay toppled and broken, the plants all dead. Moreover, everything lay under a layer of dust and dirt of a hundred years. There was no doubt he was in the same place, because over the arch he saw the name he had seen before – Omni Somnia. Had he known that the latin words given their proper construction of Omni (sunt) somnia meant that "Everything is a dream" as if emulating a similar Shakespearean saying, he might have stopped there. But he did not know the meaning then. So he went into the room on the second floor where he had been with the two dead sisters and there was still the same disorder to be found. Over the layer of dust he found his cigar case. Only now, it was marked as if branded by a red hot iron – one word which was a name – Bismilla.

The possibility of these two stories having generated from the same occurrance with variations being brought in by time cannot be ruled out. But the two houses had existed in two different parts of Valletta. Their stories had similarily retained a different following.

It was a different case with a monastic styled house in Sliema which for some time in the nineteenth century had been the home and headquarters of a sect headed by an unfrocked Italian priest – a Dr Achilli. When this sect was brought to Malta to convert its people to the "Italian Protestant Church" its mission inevitably failed, notwithstanding the wide distribution of the Protestant Bible, loaves and money in the way of a shilling to all who took the bible. It was characteristic of the Maltese to listen to all that was said, then take the loaf to eat and the money to spend, but they would throw the unread bible away. Nobody had ever enticed them away from their religion. And nobody will.

There is no record of what ultimately happened to Dr Achilli, but the ghostly restless footsteps of someone from his sect (if they weren't his) kept being heard in the courtyard of the house that had temporarily been his home.

The story of a haunted house gains importance when it is complete and giving also the originator of the haunting. I was lucky to find such an impressive story.

Victoria had to go back to her younger days in the late thirties to recall the story. She had then ran a lucrative lodging house in the city of Senglea. This was before the sluttish fingers of modern minded developers had swamped the historical loveliness of that place beneath a rash of new buildings. It was at a time too when the lodging house and its adjoining bar were well patronized by officers and men of the many British naval ships that were always in Grand Harbour. Some of them being moored only a stone's throw away.

It was a must to have a maid then. To clean the place all over, day in day out, and do other chores. Sometimes there was more than one. But this story concerned Claire, the permanent woman. Strong, clean and jolly, who would cheerfuly make short work of her chores every day to hurry home and meet her sweetheart whom she was going to marry.

But one day it was a different Claire who reported for work. The cheerful look which had become part of her could be seen no more on her face. Something was wrong. When Victoria asked her what was ailing her all she would say was that everyone had his problems. What had indeed happened was that her boy-friend had jilted her. But she would not tell anyone. Instead, she went upstairs, and there was nothing to indicate that she was not starting her daily work. This time, however, she did not stop on any of the floors where work awaited her. She kept going up, straight on to the roof. Then from there she hurled herself into the internal court-yard.

Victoria knew what was happening when she heard her piercing scream as she fell down, and the bang when she hit the ground to kill herself.

She loved Claire and knew that she would never forget her. Indeed she couldn't, because after then there was to be a continuous replay of that last highly emotional moment of the girl. There would be her piercing scream with the same tell-tale rising pitch and then the bang as she had hit the ground.

Somehow that haunting was not so irritating to Victoria since she knew what was behind it. But when there were others to hear the replay and would fearfully ask what was happening, Victoria would answer: "That was poor Claire."

There were other houses isolated from society in the three cities of the Knights, Vittoriosa, Cospicua and Senglea; in Valletta the capital, the more recent Sliema, and also in cosmopolitan Balżan, all having their particular stories of possession by denizens of the spiritual world. The Inquisitor's Palace at Għirġenti once a majestic building partly of the twelfth and partly of the seventeenth century was like a creeper-covered Georgian country house, lying all alone in a wild country side which can be as spooky as it is beautiful, and burdened wit legendary stories of restless spirits including a spiteful Torquemada. But if this was only a legend, why was this beautiful place abandoned to waste and be torn apart by vandals?

It seemed that for what part ghostly manifestations had to play in Maltese life and heritage, the ground had been prepared so well as if by some press agent, which was not to be ignored. The spring of public attention was wound, and a great many people could make use of it, if it were to be unravelled. This was the feeling which raised a silent clamour of indignation and imbued me with the will to follow more avidly the manifestations in the house at Paola.

Until then I had supported the touching faith of those living in that house who prayed for the manifestations to cease. Even if this meant reproaching what cynicism still lurked about them. But now that I was all eager to go deeper into and study the manifestations further, they suddenly stopped.

I did not know how and why this had come about, and I did not give much credit to a possible explanation of poltergeistic symptoms limiting themselves in time as if the energy supply used in them is spent up, and has to be regenerated. Whatever it was, there appeared a ray of light in that house in those days. From ghosts with their manifestations of dread everyone in that family was glad to turn to brighter days. Myself included since Adeline and I began to look forward to our wedding. Ghosts or not, that house began ticking with preparations. Then the big day came on one simmering hot August morning which brought back the gaiety to the family which had oozed out during the haunted years. We had two months of married happiness in a house of our own which made us forget all the phantasmagoria we had been subjected to. With the new bliss of married life my anxieties and intentions towards the supernatural seemed to have evaporated. Had anybody mentioned ghosts to me than I might have even returned to my scepticism. Then one October morning fate dealt a more tangible blow when Adeline's father died.

He was a god man, and apart from the sorrow which wife, children and familiars naturally feel in such circumstances there was none of the neurotic fancies and psychic relativities that might have been expected to be connected with his death. His, had been a peaceful life, and so was his demise. But it was then that the unexpected happened.

The ghostly forces inside that house came back. This time with an impetus that left everyone gasping for breath.

The sounds of breathing and footsteps were resumed. There was now added to them the noise of dragging chains.

"We've never had it so bad," said my brothers-in-law when they told me about it.

"It seems," said one of them, "as if the manifestations

were somehow placated by father's constant prayers when he was still with us. They have now returned with vengeance that he is no more."

It was now 1948, and the ghosts in that house began to materialise dramatically with ocular evidence for almost each person under that roof, often suspending the operation of familiar natural laws. They left no time for reasoning to those in there, and no chance for planning to me.

This time when hearing the poltergeistic disturbance or breaking crockery in the dining room as before, Frank rushed down to investigate. It was not all bravery on his part, because he was expecting to be met by the usual empty and undisturbed room as before. It turned out to be different, however, and on reaching the room he stopped short as if struck by lightning. He was overcome with fear of something from which he might have even welcomed death as an escape. He didn't see any ghosts, but the chairs which he had always known and seen stacked round the dining table were now elevated in the air as if held by unseen hands, and were moving round as in a macabre dance.

It seemed as if the poltergeist had intended to go on a teasing spree, and in the days that followed he resorted to the common poltergeistic habit of teasing with the water tap. Frank and John would hear the tap dripping in the bathroom and would go to turn it off, when it would by itself go off and stop dripping as they approached. When they went back to their room, it would start dripping again. This went on with nauseating repetitions until they would give up and let the tap drip only to hear the water running stronger when they would perforce have to go and turn it off. But if these manifestations were only in the way of causing a disquieting disturbance, there was a different and a terrifying experience for William. he heard the sound of a zinc washing tub moving, as if doing a see-saw action on being badly balanced. It never occurred to him that this might be due to some ghostly manifestation, and when he went to steady the tub he saw the tail of a cat protruding out, and assumed it was the animal that was moving that tub. What he should have realized and didn't in that tense moment was that there were no cats in the house. But when he took hold of the cat's tail intending to swing it out of the tub he was shocked with freezing horror as he saw that it had a man's face.

The other brother George did little or no interventions during these manifestations. He had a crucifix hanging over his bed to which he said his prayers, then covered his face with the blankets and alternated between sleeping and laying awake listening to what was going on around him. But he was stupefied into silence when very often on emerging from his blankets in the morning and turned to the crucifix to say his prayers of thanksgiving, he found it covered with bile as if some being had manifested its desperation or hatred by spitting the vile mucus on the holy figure.

These manifestations went on day after day and as they were being recounted to me with all the seriousness they merited hoping that I would think of something or some move to alleviate the situation, I found myself at a loss and what imagination I could already control in those days as I can do now, was then stampeding. However I was convinced that if there was a place where exorcism was required, that surely was the one. I had them check with the previous tenants of that house who were found and confirmed that they had also been haunted when they lived there, although not in such a grand scale. Fearing no lawsuit or libel, they also confronted the landlord and with his reply and attitude hinted that he knew about the ghostly influences on his house. I was convinced then that the only possible way out of the situation, if they could not leave that house, was to exorcise it.

It was agreed to take my advice but it seemed that the ghosts also intended to circumvent it, and they launched what was to be their final assault as if destined to send the people under that roof to either death or a lunatic asylum. Certainly to damnation.

They started with Carmelina, my sister-in-law, who had an even worst fright than her original one of years back when one night she felt someone getting into her bed. Before she knew it she found the same South American looking youth she had seen in the mirror on that first occasion. He was now smiling at her. But it was more a malicious snigger than a smile. She wanted to scream but found she couldn't because of the fear that clogged her throat. She tried to move and exert force to push him away, but she lay as if in invisible chains.

"Oh God. What can I do?" she remembers saying to herself.

"Don't try to resist," her instinct told her, "it's useless – just pray." But before she could gather her scattered thoughts to do so, she felt the ghost's lips on her cheek. There was warmth in that kiss, but not of the kind associated with a man kissing a woman. It was a vile sensation. As hot as the fire of hell, and as desperate as the spirit which was behind it. When the spell broke, she rose up and ran to the bathroom feeling tainted and unclean. Desperately she washed her face at the wash-basin, over and over again, as if water could wash away also her feelings. Then she looked at the mirror and knew the truth. Where the ghastly lips had touched her cheek there was the mark. It was an imprint as that branded on cattle by red-hot iron.

She was not to know then that the brand was to remain with her for months, to be seen by doctors and priests, and that only time would make it disappear to leave only its dreadful effect in memory. Even to-day, thirty two years after, there is still the occasional tingling in her cheek where that mark had been, as a reminder of that dramatic episode.

But there was more of the bizarre to follow on that fateful night. Carmelina had stopped looking in the mirror not believing her eyes. Her fingers touched the scar in her face then stiffened with fright as she belatedly realized the full truth. She would probably have broken down had she not heard the sigh. She recognised her mother's voice. Indeed there had been occasions when she and her brothers had distinctly heard their mother calling them during the night and found her asleep when they went to her. This could have been a similar ghostly stratagem. But being only a sigh she heard, it could have also been uttered in a dream. Yet, she had sensed there was much more in it than that. It had been like a pitiful call for help.

Shocked as she was she made an effort and ran to her mother in another room. By the dim light of a small night lamp in front of a holy picture she saw her mother was asleep, although the nervous twitching of her eyelids and the low sigh she heard her utter spelt restlessness. Then suddenly there was something moving at the side of the bed where the light was fainter.

It began like something unstable and undefined, materializing out of darkness. Then in a flash it assumed the form of a woman in black. Carmelina stood petrified with terror not even daring to breathe as she regarded the ghost's Victorian clothes of an earlier period, and the distorted face dead white with rage. The mouth was open, and even the lips were drawn back to show the savage white teeth. Then her heart stopped dead as she saw the woman in black bending over the helpless form of her mother in the pose of the legendary Dracula when looking for a place where to sink his fangs.

The mettle of this girl in confront with the supernatural has already been made evident when it involved only her. Now, the proximity of danger to her mother gave her more resource to act immediately. Forgetting the possibility of any personal danger she went on to arouse her and moved her away to the obvious disdainful look that appeared in the face of the spectral woman.

The news of that night's commotion soon spred to the other members of the family who were not resident there. Myself included. Without any pre-arrangement we all assembled there on the morning after the night of debacle. Everyone was expressing his own opinion. There was also Carmelo, the eldest son who was married and lived on his own. He was the only remaining sceptic of the lot, and even after hearing what had happened he would still, like the biblical St Thomas, not believe anything that was being said.

Suddenly there was screaming from upstairs. It was Maurice, ten year old, who was the youngest, and who was left sleeping in his bed. His pitiful and mad screaming jerked us into action. Carmelo and I were the first to rush upstairs to find the bewildered boy mesmerized into terror with his bed being forcefully pushed by a door against which it stood, opening and closing by itself with obviously no one being visible behind it. I lifted the boy in my arms and ran downstairs with him where I left him to the care of his mother and sister. When all was said and done, none had anything further to say. This last episode had come like a confirmation of all our conversation which had all been about leaving that house in preference to exorcising it. All became quiet as the grave.

Even Carmelo who was always poking fun and disbelief at what was said was now strangely silent. Then he pulled me aside.

"There is no further scope for disbelief," he said, "I know now that there are ghosts in this house."

I did not need him to tell me that, but coming from a stubborn sceptic like him his words meant a lot.

"So you have been persuaded now that you've seen the state of your brother," I said, thinking that was what had made him see the truth.

"No, it wasn't that" he said. Then after pausing as if to think of his next words he continued. "Didn't you see her as we went into the boy's room?"

I had to confess that I did not see anyone or anything.

"She was a woman, all dressed in black," he said, "and she was sitting on the first stair leading to the second floor, almost blocking our entrance to the room. She was crying."

I stood there nonplussed at his words. The he continued: "When we went in both of us passed right through her."

I did not know whether it was what he said that made me think of the whiff of coldness I thought I felt as I went into that room. Then I was suddenly feeling it again.

Those weren't days when residence could be changed in a jiffy. The housing problem was still at a crucial stage. So whether they liked it or not there had to be some more days and nights to be spent in that house. But they could still in the meantime resort to exorcism. With the men at work, the children at school and the women out on their shopping most of the days would somehow be endured. But it would be different with the nights. And there was one coming with all that could be expected. So they made what preparations they could think of. They moved all the beds again in one bedroom, and they would sleep with the lights on. They also arranged for a cousin of the family who was unafraid of ghosts to sleep in the house that night. But as the hours crawled, expectation grew, and one could feel the tension building up. On the morrow, it was decided, they would get a priest to carry out exorcism.

But the morrow never came. When the cousin arrived to join them for the night he had his first surprise on finding the door wide open when he had been told it would be closed and was in fact given a key so that he could make his way in. He made a hubbub of what seemed to him to have been carelessness in leaving the door open. William tried to explain to him that he had himself closed and locked the door, but his words remained unsaid when there was the shrill of the door-bell ringing. They all looked at each other in silence not daring to venture a thought as to who could have been at the door at such a time. It was eleven. Taking matters in hand Carmelina went downstairs and opened the door. But there was nobody there.

Hardly had she returned upstairs and told her mother about it when again there was the ringing of the bell. None knew what to do, and in the silence that followed one could hear the thumping of hearts in a race of excitement as if in expectation to some impending drama. Carmelina went down again to open the door, and for the second time there was nobody there. Back she went upstairs when for the third time there was the shrilling of the bell. Emmanuela lost her temper, and said to them all: "Let it be. We shall not open the door now. Not even if the devil himself was behind it."

To everyone's surprise, hardly had she mentioned the devil when the ghosts came.

There were first the usual sounds of breathing close to anybody who was lying in bed. Footsteps were heard climbing the stairs, and dragging chains behind them. There was also a new noise all over the house as of a huge canvas billowing in the wind. The strongman cousin was aroused from his bed where he was already lying, and began searching for his shirt and tie which he was sure had been left hanging on a chair's back. He thought it was some joke when he found both well tacked in a night pot. But no one had the mind and will to joke in those days, and much less that night.

Emmanuela had moved out of the room for something, and Carmelina decided to go after her with a premonition of danger that might befall her. It was then that a hand appeared from nowhere and slapped her hard on the face.

When she finally went out of the room she stopped petrified with horror. There was her mother coming up the stairs; and following closely behind her there was the woman in black, looking dead intent on harming her. Carmelina would have screamed had she could, but fear blocked her throat. There seemed nothing to do except go to her mother's assistance. With another of her thoughtless actions she ran to the stairs, and placed herself between her mother and the spectre that was following her, saying nothing not to alarm her since she was not aware of the ghost. Close to her fear Carmelina's next difficulty was to refrain from looking back into the face of the diabolic woman spectre behind her, whose cold and clammy touch she felt on her shoulder as if asking her to move away so that she could get at the other.

By midnight the atmosphere inside that house became like hell and a hundred spirits seemed to have been let loose. Noises, footsteps, chains, banging doors and flitting spectres. It became so fearful that it became impossible for any human in his senses to stay there and keep sane. All the members of the family had reached the limit. It was then that they broke down. With only the clothes they had on, they left there and then. They went to sleep with relatives, and never entered that house again.

The most significant points for the case of ghosts came out soon after this dramatic end. First the Church authorities who do not pronounce themselves on such matters so easily accepted the fact that the house had been haunted. To follow in their footsteps then came the administrative authorities, even more sceptic and selective, to offer alternative accommodation. I believe this was the first time that accommodation was provided under such circumstances.

This case became news amongst the people in the

vicinity, and there were those who relented and volunteered information about the past of the house. Haunting experiences were traced to at least three previous tenants with different variants in apparitions. In one case the haunting ghost was a priest who used to materialize at the top of the first flight of stairs (where the woman in black first appeared) and on one occasion blew into the ear of the tenant of the time and caused him a shock from which he never recovered, and died.

But the most important and conclusive bit came from a neighbour who produced an old picture of a woman and a young man who had once lived in that house.

"There they are," shouted Carmelina on seeing them. "Those were the two that haunted us."

Surely enough, the two figures in that picture which she had never seen before tallied exactly with her previous descriptions of the woman in black and the young man.

If it was a timely end for those who left that house just when they could take no more, it was also a decisive climax for those close and near to change opinion about the existence of ghosts. These did not include the neighbours as they knew of other houses in that same street that were haunted, they said. They mentioned so many that for a time it seemed the whole block was infested. Even to this there were no disclaimers.

There was a silent but none the less excited welcome when an English lady went to look for accommodation in that street. She looked at the closed house. Then somebody told her it was abandoned, but never the less it wasn't fit for habitation because it was badly haunted. The lady laughed at them. Not in scorn or disbelief she assured them, but because she was a connoisseur of myth and supernatural trivia. She was a medium, she said, and possessed a high level of extra sensory perception. It was a pity she was not in time to have at least tried that house. The neighbours agreed. So she took the next best which was a room with the family living next door. There had never been any mention of ghosts in that house, and the only known occurrance which had ever disturbed the previous tenants had been the death of a five year old girl. Unloved and ill treated by her step mother which even to a so young a girl must have caused some anguish, she was killed when her father lifted her on to his horse as he often did, and unwarily released his hold that little too soon. The girl fell off the horse and was killed instantly.

It had been a tragic accident long forgotten. It was only revived for the English lady who spent only one night in that house which she had to endure terrified and exhausted by the sight of a young girl riding a horse down the stairs.

It was another case for the ghosts of Malta. One other story for the sceptics, many of whom were then not even in their cradles, to deride.

For me it was the conclusion of a debacle for conviction.

Chapter 4
Spirits with a Purpose

One type of ghost Maltese sceptics do not openly reject is that which belongs to the dead returning to rectify a wrong or ask for intercessory prayers in suffrage. It will be noted that this is an occasion when haunting departs from the scientific stage and encroaches more on the religious plane, pertaining to the immortality of the soul and its after death existence in paradise or hell. The theological truth which is more often reflected and applies in such cases is that of the existence of a purgatorial stage through which the soul can be aided in its passage of expiation to paradise by prayers and masses to be purposely said for its repose, by those still living. To those of catholic faith this is a proven truth, and the Maltese being of such faith will be the last to raise any doubts however reasonable they may appear. Even if their beliefs should concern a ghost.

Indeed, ghosts of this type must obviously be of the "one – off" kind in that they haunt on a single or particular occasion, and never appear again after getting or achieving what they are after. Because of this particularity they cannot be verified other than by the good faith and reliability of those who meet them, sometimes aided by the verifiction of facts evolved when these are available. It is because of this that I had to find some of my cases from the records of Ġużè

Diacono, a local writer who carried out a certain amount of research on Maltese ghosts.

My first case concerns a well known Maltese Capuchin monk who was detailed to preach and conduct a course of spiritual exercises to a Maltese community in Tunisia.

The first handful of Maltese had made a home in that country many years back and as was to be expected their number increased, with many eventually moving to places where other Maltese lived feeling it was a much more sober and austere kind of life for them even if the place of their choice happened to be some village off the beaten track.

It was in fact such a village that was to host the Maltese monk for his religious mission. The first difficulty, maybe the only one, that faced him and the two novices he took with him was to find lodging, and he had no choice when it was suggested to him to try and obtain the temporary use of an empty house from a shopkeeper who owned it.

"But," said the shopkeper when the monk asked him, "that house has been vacant for ages since no one would stay in it."

"Why?" asked the monk.

"I don't know," said the shopkeeper with a simple gravity that indicated the opposite. "But there is something," he continued in a different tone as if having second thoughts, "perhaps you being a monk, may after all put it in order."

The Capuchin got the message which might have diverted him from his intentions had the situation been different, but as things were, his was a Hobson's choice.

When he went to see the place he found it was an old house in a plat of dry weeds and two caressing palm trees. Drab brick houses were in the vicinity, mud roofs, and the smell of camel's dung on the wind. The outlook was indeed as foreboding as the shopkeeper's words had hinted. But the pious intentions behind his mission prevailed over his human frailty.

Indeed when he and the two novices moved in that night they had finished a hard day between setting things straight in the house itself and their work at the church.

There was only time for a light quickly cooked meal, and prayers. Then they shot the rusty bolts on the door and the novices went to bed, dog-tired, falling asleep as they hit the pillow.

But the monk would not sleep. He couldn't. He took pencil and paper and tried jotting down some notes on the morrow's sermon. The unnatural silence of the place bred in him an undefinable restlessness. He knew that a breeze was blowing but it won not the least responsive whisper from the trees outside. As he sat and tried to work in the mellow gloom saved from total darkness by the poor light of an oil lamp he was straining his ears to listen for some sound that would normalize the atmosphere around him. But there was not a whisper beyond the thumping of his heart. It seemed as if life was standing still. When it became late with no evident change, he put away his notes and took up the breviary to read the office for the day. It was then that there was a heavy knock on the door.

"Good gracious," exclaimed the monk, this being the strongest expletive he could use even though he was startled out of his wits. When he could compose himself but for his chattering teeth and the chilly feeling that seemed to pervade the very marrow in his bones he called feebly:

"Who is there?"

"It's us," said a somewhat rough voice from outside. "Open up".

The monk hesitated, thinking vaguely that the voice he heard could not after all belong to the supernatural that has been filling his head and heart. But if it didn't, then who could the callers be if he didn't know anyone in the country to which he was a stranger? Then he thought of his mission. It could be that someone needed his help, albeit it was a strange time to call for it. Maybe it was a dying man who wanted the last sacraments. With this thought his courage returned and he made to rise up and go to the door. But it seemed that he had dallied too long for the callers' impatience.

"If you don't open," came the same rough voice from outside, "we can be with you all the same."

He knew now that after all this was no normal call, and beset again by the trembling fear of before he opened the door.

There were two men outside who without a further word pushed past him into the room. He could now see them better. The elder of the two who had a long beard must have looked well over his sixties; the other looked a little younger. He wanted to ask them what they wanted but his voice failed him. But he needn't have bothered.

"Take up pencil and paper, and write," said the elder man to him in what could be termed an angry tone.

Now overtaken by a shivering tremble the like of which he had never known, the monk sat down at the table to do what he was being bidden.

"What shall I write?" he asked feebly with what voice he could muster.

"Tell the shopkeeper who owns this house that when he inherited it he knew that I had begotten it by foul means," dictated the old man. "My son here," he continued, pointing to the other that was with him, "knew this as well."

There was a moment's pause during which the silence that prevailed in the room was broken only by the sound of pencil moving on paper as the monk hastily wrote what was said.

"If after knowing this," continued the old man, "he will not give this house back to the family who is the rightful owner, then he will one day suffer . . . as both of us are doing."

As the monk continued writing, now fully aware that the two men with him were the ghosts of the dead returned to right a wrong they had done in their lifetime, it occurred to him that he would need a witness to what was happening if he were to be believed. He thought of the novices, but rejected the idea of waking them up not to frighten them. Then he thought of something.

"Will you sign what I wrote?" he asked the older man when he was ready.

Without a further word the bearded one took up the pencil and signed. And where the pencil touched paper it burned through it.

The following morning, the monk carried out the dreadful message to the shopkeeper who later complied with the request. The house was freed of its encumbrance. The capuchin had reason to remember the frightening experience of that night for ever by the shivering tremble which begot him, and remained with him for the rest of his life as a witness to his story.

Another case from Ġużè Diacono's records concerns the ghost of a priest. It began with some residents of Bull Street in Cospicua (Malta) happening to look through a window into the house of a neighbour Cetta Cordina and seeing her lying unconscious on the floor. When they went in to help her, and Cetta regained consciousness she related what had happened. It seemed that for a long time she had been hearing sounds of human groaning from an inner room in her house. Assuming it was the characteristic *hares* she had got so used to it that she was not bothering about it any longer. On the day of the incident however, either because the groaning became more persistent or because of a bad mood, she rushed into the inner room brandishing the iron with which she was ironing clothes at that time, and shouted at whoever was groaning to shut up.

With the suddenness of a lightning flash, she said, there erupted a big fire which lighted the whole room, and enveloped in the leaping flames she saw the ghost of a priest, who was a canon she knew and who had been dead for some years. It was then that she fainted.

The story might have ended there, being attributed to some hallucination or a made up fantastic tale. But Michael, the woman's father realised that there might be more behind the apparition which he believed his daughter had. He felt it was something to be investigated by a priest, and he went to one. The priest went to Cetta's house with thoughts of exorcism, but when the ghost of the canon manifested itself and spoke to him he knew he did not have to deal with a damned spirit. The ghost told the investigating priest of Masses that had to be said for his repose and which were forgotten. He even referred him to an entry made in the acts of a public notary which laid down this obligation and was not carried out. The investigating priest who also knew the dead canon took it as his responsibility to see into the matter, and after verifying the entry as indeed it existed in the acts of the mentioned notary (whom I happened to know myself) took steps for the Masses to be said.

With rectification, the apparations of the ghost, and also the groaning stopped altogether.

In an almost similar case, rectification of an error was brought about by the ghost of a dead monk before the lapse was committed. The person involved was another monk who was entrusted with detailing the masses to be said in his priory. One day, after preparing the list for the morrow he retired to his cell where to his utter surprise he saw the ghost of a monk he knew to have been dead. Instantaneously he remembered that there was to be a Mass said for the repose of the soul of the dead monk on the morrow, which he had forgotten to put on the list.

A most interesting story which could provide a new insight into the element of ghosts is that of a haunting occurring in a town called St Vennera in Malta. Until some years ago this was only a suburb, and there were hardly enough houses and inhabitants to make up a parish. It was only years after the last war that a small town of clean white stone buildings rose up where there had previously been fields and open spaces. Although close in kilometres to other inhabited areas, as indeed all towns and villages to Malta are, it is centuries apart in atmosphere. If there is a place where one would not expect any lurking ghosts, it would be St Vennera. Indeed, it might have been such a kind of assumption that in 1955 made Mrs Julia Tanti ignore the sounds of a human voice crying and groaning in one particular room in her house between 4.30 and 5 in the morning. Being at such an early hour when more likely than not all would be still asleep, this manifestation might have even been taken for a dream. But when the ghostly voice began uttering intelligible words expressing suffering there was no more question of dreaming. When the children began to hear the ghost too, for by now all knew there was one, Mrs Tanti was bold enough to ask the unknown haunter what was it that he wanted. But to her question there was never a reply.

When she could bear it no longer she decided to talk to the Parish Priest about it. Before she could do so however, one of her daughters woke up from her sleep screaming one morning, and when she could speak in between sobbing, said that the ghost had spoken to her more than the usual words. It was expected that what promised to be a remarkable first hand account of the haunting should arouse interest. And so it did, both with the Parish Priest to whom Mrs Tanti now went with the whole story, and also with the Monsignor who was asked to investigate with a view of considering exorcism.

"My name is Joseph Mangion," the invisible ghost had said to the daughter, "and I am 66 years old. I am suffering so much." Then he had asked her to go and tell everything to relatives of his who lived in the nearby town of Ħamrun. He did not give an address, but pointed out that these relatives lived opposite the Radio City Theatre which was indeed in Ħamrun.

The Monsignor had decided this was no case for exorcism, and the Parish Priest advised Mrs Tanti to try and contact the people indicated by the ghost.

No one in the Tanti's household knew anyone by the name of Mangion. Neither dead nor alive, but they knew where the Radio City Theatre was. Living just opposite, they found a widow by that surname. She told them that Joseph Mangion had been her late husband's brother who had died in Sliema when he was 20 years old, and that he had been dead for 44 years, which was well before she knew her late husband. It registered with them that had Joseph Mangion remained alive he would have been 66 years old. This seemed to indicate the truth in what his ghost had spoken. Mrs Mangion did no deny the fact even though she never knew the dead man.

It will here be noticed that even though the dead man had died in a different town and place, the location of his relatives was pinpointed with precision, even to mentioning the landmark of the Radio City Theatre which was built many years after his death. Moreover, when Joseph Mangion had died, the widow to whom he referred the people he haunted after his death, had not yet known his brother.

That all this was devised in a ghostly beyond is neither surmise nor intelligent guessing. But if this ghost had manifested what could be termed as intelligence, why has it haunted a family who was not in the least involved with what he was after, rather than chasing the people he wanted in the first place?

One could draw various conclusions in answer to this question, though all of them must be influenced by what one knows and believes about psychic phenomena. The fact that in the Tanti family there were two priests and three nuns lends a Maltese belief that the ghost chose a family which could supply the prayers he wanted in suffrage. A more likely reason is related to the very important factor which I have mentioned in that certain people alone have the power to see or hear ghosts; and his only relative might have well belonged to the type that does not have this power and made him resort to someone else who had. But whichever of the two answers, or any other might have applied, there is no doubt whatsoever that the ghost was in search of prayers in suffrage which as has been evidenced in other cases generally consist of Masses to be said.

With this kind of ghosts there is no dichotomy to puzzle anyone. Hadn't the Church in Malta acquiscied, and indeed administered the payment in one's lifetime for Masses to be said for his soul's repose after death? Admittedly this scheme had the double purpose of providing for priests through the stipendia they are paid for the masses they say; but the fact remains that thousands of pounds, maybe millions, were at some time or other placed into such a scheme which has paid for the thousands of masses that have been said in Malta's multitude of churches since hundreds of years ago. Indeed all the masses that are still being said today, in an even bigger number of churches are also paid for in this way. Aren't there also the multiferous wills in notarial acts wherein features the most obvious clause outlining how many masses are to be said and where for the repose of the testate's soul after his death? And the many pious acts and prayers willed to individuals and institutions which are conditioned to donations by dead donors. Truly enough this is an episode of Maltese usage sounding more like an attempt for reassurance and security of one's soul after death. It smacks of an artful blend of religion and personal insurance. But the fact remains that the purpose and effect behind the genuinely made offers is an undeniable truth.

The most important point to be stressed is however that all this is subject to the risk of some of these commitments escaping one's attentions which very often bring about the supernatural reminders as have been exemplified.

John Pisani recounted to me how when his aunt who was his mother's sister went to stay with his parents in their house at Birkirkara she was constantly being disturbed by the sound of moving furniture in the room which was above her own. This being his father's room, his aunt reached the conclusion that his father was purposely moving his furniture about to disturb her as she was probably not wanted there.

Remarking about this to her sister she was assured this was not the case, and also when his father got to know of it he refuted any ulteriour motives. Indeed he denied that he had ever moved any furniture about.

When the woman could bear it no longer she had resort to one of the priests in the parish who found the right ocasion to talk to the father about it. There was the same denial again, and the priest believed him. It was now he reached the conclusion that the disturbance must have had a supernatural origin. So he suggested that there should be some masses said. John's father gave the priest some money to say what masses he suggested, and when this was done the disturbances stopped.

John's father never understood these things, but when some time later he found a ready purchaser for his house who was offering good money he agreed to sell it. As is normally done in such cases a deed of promise was entered with a notary which would make the sale materialise after three months during which researches are made to ensure there are no outstanding burdens on the acquisition of property before it can be sold. In this case to everyone's surprise the notary declared that the sale could not be effected because of a burden which he had not declared to him.

"What is this burden you speak of?" asked John's father.

"It's the saying of one mass every year for the repose of the first owner of the house," replied the notary.

"But I know of no such burden," he said to the notary, "and throughout the years I have lived in that house I never had any Masses said." Then he added on second thoughts, "Except once."

He stopped there as he remembered the disturbances there had been, and how they had ceased after he had Masses said. He knew too that the priest and the notary were not aware of each other's part in the cse, and had acted independently. This made him a little wiser.

For a good twelve years I had my office in a house in one of the many narrow streets of Valletta which from the centre that had been the top of the hill on which the Knights had built the city run down deep into the guts which make the periphery. Like many others it could be aptly called a house of ghosts in a web of grey streets. A drab lobby, and a wide built-in staircase reflect its period. But there are high ceilinged rooms, tall windows, good stone chimney-places, and rambling rooms upstairs which lead in and out like a rabbit warren.

Over the door to the main hall there is an inscription on marble which many a plasterer and white washer throughout the last four centuries had refrained from covering up when working on the building's maintenance. The inscription reads as follows:

Il. V. Com. Fr. Giambattista Galeano Chateauneuf della Ven. Ling. di Provenza posseditore che fu di questa casa in testamento la lascio ai nipoti sotto la condizione che dopo la loro morte, fosse all commenda di Nizza incorporata col peso che chiunque avesse quella commenda facesse dire due messe in ciascuna ebdomada

Dagli atti Pubblici
di Pietro Vella Notaro
11 Maggio 1631

Testimoni
Fr. Giov. Paolo Lascaris
E.F. G. Battista del Pozzo

Its translation in English reads thus:

The Venerable Commendatore (title) Brother

Giambattista Galeano Chateauneuf of the Venerable Langue of Provence who is the owner of this house leaves it in his will to his nephews under the condition that after their death it shall through the commendation of Nice be burdened with the obligation that whoever shall have such commendation (the house) will have two masses said in every Holy Week.

From the Public Acts
of Pietro Vella Notary
11 May 1631

Witnesses
Brother Giov. Paolo Lascaris
E.F.G. Battista del Pozzo

Apart from its value in throwing light on the long usage of burdening buildings with masses to be said which is here evidenced to go back to the time of the Knights, the inscription which is a true copy of a notarial act lends to the thought as to whether or not the masses laid down are still being said to fullfill the burden. The building to-day belongs to government like many others, similar in history and perhaps also in burden. A likely question is whether this house is haunted.

Joseph Bonnici, who spent the best years of his life working in there was convinced it was. On one particular occasion when he was in the building with only one other person as if to serve as witness he was violently pushed down the stairs. More recent than this there were three female clerks working late when through the open door of the room one of them saw the shadowy figure of a man crossing a corridor. She screamed only to have the others turning on her for startling them out of their wits because of what they had assumed was only a hallucination. But when a second girl saw the same shadowy figure cross the same corridor soon after there was no more room for doubt.

There was also the occasion of Mr Cherrett, a messenger who had very often to stay late with the departmental head when all the other members of the staff had left. On this particular occasion he answered the bell by which the head called him to his office. Only to be told that he was not wanted and that no one had rang. He might have thought he had imagined it all had there not be the indicator falling to show the number confirming that the bell must have been rung from the push button on the head's desk. He was still wondering about it when for the second time there was the bell – and again the indicator falling. Again he went to his head, now astonished and not understanding how the bell could have rung if he had not pressed the push. When for the third time there was a repetition of this manifestation, the head decided it was time to leave.

He might have been thinking that his messenger had after all thought of a sure way to make him jittery, and he began to tell him so as they walked down the stairs, together. On their way out there was then the bell ringing again – this time with its shrilling reverbrating all over the place as if to draw attention to whoever must have been pressing the push inside the room which the head had locked and carried the key with him. There was a pause as the two men stopped and looked at each other as if to pass a message – one that he was wrong, and the other that had been right. Then without a further word they rushed outside as the bell was still shrilling its ghostly message.

The head is to-day no more since he died some years ago, but the messenger is still alive to recount and confirm all this. The bell is still on the same wall, and the push where it had been then – on the same desk and in the same room – which for a time were my own.

The Church, however, exercises a meticulous care with this matter of Masses. The same can be said of the clergymen wo are involved. This is epitomised by a story concerning St John's Cathedral in Valletta.

This gem of a church was built by Grand Master La Cassiere between 1573 and 1578 on the design of Maltese architect Girolamo Cassar. It became the Conventual Church of the Order of St John of Jerusalem, and following La Cassiere's allocation of a chapel to each of the national Langues of the Order, enticed the richest and most powerful houses in Europe at that time to vie with each other for the whole of 200 years to embellish their representative chapels. The priceless altar pieces and the sumptuous frescoes of the ceiling by Mattia Preti, harmonising with the Flemish tapestries with designs by Rubens invoke an aura of splendour, detached from the world of ghosts. The only sense of haunting in St John's is where it is shed by the beautiful canvasses by Caravaggio, the magnificent silver by Bernini and the incomparable alabaster by Puget. But . . .

A sexton at the cathedral respected all the clergymen with whom his duties brought him in contact. However, he grew to have a special sentiment towards a particular monsignor. Strangely enough, it might have come out of pity than from anything else. He pitied the exemplary clergyman who never seemed depressed, never complained of life or duties in which he never faltered, and always kept away from the limelight. The sexton pitied the monsignor in fact, because he wanted so little. That was why he made it a point never to fail being on time to serve him in his daily first mass of the day which he said at five in the morning.

This was at a time when mass was celebrated in the Latin rite, being a simple coordinated service between celebrant and server. At such an early time of the day when it was often still dark outside they were always alone in the sagristy, and the intercourse between the two men which developed into being singularly close became like a drill. The sexton would open the church at half past four, prepare the altar and go into the sagristy by quarter to five when the monsignor would arrive on the dot. They would then chat as the priest is helped to don his vestments. At five o'clock mass will begin. This must have been going on certainly for many months, maybe years, with always the same routine never varying, until each one of them began to anticipate what would occur during their daily interlude, even to the extent of what was to be said.

Then one day something changed. The sexton arrived as usual and began doing what he had always done. When the monsignor arrived, punctual as always, there was missing the usual greeting. The sexton said the words himself. But there was no reply. So he began to wonder why. He helped the priest with his vestments, and perhaps more than before took pains to start a conversation. Yet, not a word escaped the priest's lips. The sexton could not understand what had happened, and much as he tried to read something behind his look, he did not succeed. He knew the priest had surprisingly changed; gravely changed. It seemed to him that the monsignor might have also been averting to look at him, and what efforts were being made towards this were making him look nervous and fidgety.

Mass was said as usual. When it was finished and both men returned to the sagristy it was the same story all over again. Now convinced that the priest was beset by some private matter which was after all not his business, the sexton refrained from saying a word. Then, as the monsignor was leaving through the side door he turned abruptly to the sexton and spoke to him. But his words were not of the expected explanation or salutation. All he said was: "See that you will come here as usual tomorrow."

Then he strode away, leaving the sexton gaping in surprise, not understanding why the monsignor should after having kept so strangely silent throughout the time they were together, say anything so banal.

Natural light began pouring through the high window in the sagristy as dawn opened the sky outside. The sexton looked at his watch and hurried in the direction of the belfry to peal the time bell for the six o'clock mass. Crossing the church there was the priest who would be celebrating it. Unlike other occasions when he would walk straight to the sagristy the priest stopped to talk to the sexton. There was an apparent look of anxiety on his face. The he asked about the previous mass that must have been missed.

"Missed?" asked the sexton, not understanding what was being said. "Why should it have been missed?"

Then the priest broke the news of the Monsignor's death. The sexton was stunned. When he found his voice he said: "But how could it be? He left here only ten minutes ago."

The priest looked at him in silence. This time it was him who could not understand. Then as if to drive in his point he said: "But the Monsignor died at midnight."

A mixed feeling of horror and consternation seized the sexton and made him go suddenly dumb. Just when he most wanted to talk. It seemed to him then that someone was going mad. To escape that ambiguous moment and have the chance to think clearly he walked to the belfry, thinking on the way how that morning's illusion could have been possible. But he was soon remembering the strange attitude of the monsignor, and how he had been convinced of his grave change. If he had indeed died at midnight, and he had no reason not to believe this, then he could understand such change in that all throughout the time he had not been with the monsignor. But with his ghost.

He felt a wave of coldness pervading throughout his body, even though it had dawned a warm day. Then he remembered of the dead priest's request before he left. Notwithstanding all natural inclinations to the contrary he was suddenly determined to comply with it, and keep the appointment.

He was at the sagristy as usual on the following day. With him there was another monsignor. He had not liked the idea of this second person being there, since, he thought, it might keep the ghostly priest away. But he needn't have worried. At quarter to five on the dot there was the quiet sound as of one coming along the passage to the sagristy. Little regular steps he had come to know so well.

"Listen," he said hoarsely to the monsignor who was with him, "he is coming."

The other nodded in affirmation. But both of them were suddenly shaking with apprehension.

When the monsignor they knew to have been dead joined them, he went straight to his place and began going through the usual movements in taking up his vestments. The two living beings stood absolutely still, looking at him from head to foot as if to see whether there was anything changed in the peron they had known so well in life, and who was now dead. There was however nothing to indicate that he was not still with the living. Yet, as both of them said later, they could feel a barrier separating them.

When they could hold their suspense no longer, the clergyman with the sexton found the necessary courage and spoke: "In the name of God monsignor, tell me, why do you come here?"

The dead monsignor turned to him this time, and with the same benevolent look, and the voice of before, he said: "It is because of three Masses I had left unsaid. To-day's being the second one, I will come again tomorrow. Then I will trouble you no more."

And so it was.

A different version of this case describes it as happening at the other cathedral at Mdina. There is also another version of people who saw the dead monsignor leaving St John's Cathedral from the side entrance. This coincides with my story, which I have written as it was reliably given to me.

If there had been reservations on the occurrances of these and many other similar apparitions it was very likely due to the characteristic Maltese sceptic strain which seems to discard sensationalism and it was certainly not for anything else. But once a haunting story is out it always enriches the local life.

Mr Frank De Domenico, a well known Maltese gentleman of Sliema recounted to me something which had happened to him in his childhood. It was 1914 to be exact. Maybe this is too far back, but with him it is as fresh as if it had only just occurred.

He was a young boy, looking at his name on the results lists of the entrance examination to the Malta Lyceum in Valletta. He was so excited to learn that he had passed and was already visualizing his coming days in that secondary school then considered of the elite. Suddenly there was someone tapping on his shoulder, and he turned round to see who it was. There was a priest, in his long black cassock, and the black hat. A common enough figure for Malta even in those days. But what shocked the boy was the face. It was drawn and thin, as if there were only the parched skin covering the skull, with the flesh totally gone. The eyes looked more than something provisionally placed in the still apparent deep sockets.

Frank's brains turned dry and hot in his head. But then the priest spoke, as if to ascertain him that he was after all a living being.

"Hullo," he said, "All right?"

"Yes," gasped Frank, "I passed."

It was pretty obvious and normal opening being made

by the mysterious priest. But the next question surprised Frank.

"Can you serve Mass?"

"Yes," said Frank. Although he could not understand the relation of the question.

"Then follow me" said the priest. And he strode away.

More by instinct than by intent Frank followed the priest, walking slowly as if to keep his distance without knowing why. A hundred yards or so farther down from the Lyceum in Merchants Street in Valletta there was then, as it still lies now, the small church dedicated to the Souls in Purgatory. That was where the priest went and waited for Frank. When he joined him the priest asked the boy to wait for him in the empty church. Without a further word he then walked into a room by the high altar which Frank assumed to have been the vestry.

The minutes flew as Frank waited. With waiting came preoccupation. He began having a feeling that everything was not all that normal, even though it had been hinted to him what was the service he was required to render. Then finally he was fed up. Maybe he had become more curious than frightened. There was only one thing to do. Walking stealthily he went to have a look in the room where the priest had gone, expecting to see him there. Possibly preparing for mass, which, he was thinking, was already delayed.

But to his utter surprise he found that the room was only a vault. Not the vestry he had expected. There was no other opening besides the door he had gone through. No windows or other apertures. And it was as empty as the rest of the building. The priest had simply disappeared.

For one brief moment he looked around him as if to ensure he had got everything right. Then as the amazing truth dawned on him, he ran out of the vault and the church, and did not stop running until he got on the bus which took him home.

His father knew the meaning behind the son's adventure. He summed it by saying to him: "By running away you might have deprived a dead priest from earning suffrage by saying a mass he still had to say on earth."

Another typical case comes from Senglea at a time which I remember. It concerned a Mrs Mangion, a woman now dead who was well known for her good demeanour and seriousness of purpose in life. Like the family woman of her time, she always made it a point to hear the first mass of the day which was at 5 a.m. This would then allow her enough time to attend to her husband and children before they leave for work and school respectively. The early mass would also afford her the time for a chat with other churchgoers, particularly when they were a little early and found St Philip Church still closed. They would then sit on the church steps to await the sexton to open up. Whether it was five minutes or ten they had to wait it did not bother them since they had began to look forward to that chat as much as the mass.

One day Mrs Mangion was earlier than her usual. She realised this by the darkness that still prevailed in the street. But rather than hesitating what to do she went on. The most she would have to do would be to wait for her friends on the church's steps. To her utter surprise, however, she found the church open.

She could not understand how this could have come about. Anyway, she could go and wait inside for her friends. Unless of course they were already there themselves.

But they weren't. There was no one to be seen in the church. Not even the sexton. There were, however, two lighted candles on the main altar, as if it were ready for mass. She registered the fact with some surprise. How could this be if the first mass was scheduled for five o'clock, and it must have been a good half an hour before the time? And where was the sexton, so that she could ask him? But there were no replies to her questions. Instead more surprises awaited her in the way of a priest who came out of the sagristy dressed in holy vestments and walking to the altar to say mass.

Apart from the candles on the altar there was no other light in church. So she could not see his face. There was nothing in that, but she was surprised to se that there was no one to serve him at mass. Not even the sexton, who would normally do the service himself when there wasn't anyone else. Still the priest started and once in there she thought she might as well hear that mass too.

As the service went on silently, being then in the old Latin ritual, Mrs Mangion folowed by saying the usual prayers she said at mass. But she could not help having occasional glances aside as if to note that no one else had entered the church. She was alone, and so she remained until the mass came to an end. It was then that the celebrant turned to face her and the aisle to give final benediction and say the "Ite Missa est", and Mrs Mangion froze with terror.

Where the priest's face should have been there was the bony skull of a dead man.

She held herself from screaming with difficulty, and felt herself going in a faint. It was then that she heard the church door being unlocked, and as from a distance the sound of talking voices coming from the people she knew who were on other days waiting with her. Before she could realise what was happening, there were the approaching footsteps of the sexton who came near her. He was as shocked to see her there as she had been.

"What are you doing here Mrs Mangion?" he asked her when he found his voice. "And how did you come in?"

"I found the door open," she began saying.

"How coud that be if I have just opened the door now?" interposed the sexton.

And true enough there were her friends coming in to ask her the same question.

But then she remembered the celebrant's skull face, and the fact that she had not seen him go into the sagristy. It had been as if he had disappeared after giving final benediction. And the chalice, the missal he used for the mass could not be seen on the altar. Even the candles were out awaiting to be lighted. It was as if she had dreamed it all.

But she knew she had not, and so did the others who listened to her story which made them shudder to hear it as she was shuddering to tell it. They all realised that she had been witness to some dead priest who had returned to say a mass he had not done in his life time.

It would not be wrong to say that the Maltese had

never stopped being a people that thrive on the occult. It had always stimulated them and gave their otherwise empty days meaning. In what concerned their religious beliefs, however, they had always looked to their Church for directions, and this is what they did in this case. Here however, it was nothing like the case of the Evil Eye, and the counteracting of its baleful effects by burning blessed olive branches, to which the Church had reacted with silent acquiesence which was immediately interpreted as agreement. So much so that when olive branches were not readily available there was the national resort to the traditional superstition of making the sign of the Horn of Mithras by pointing the index and little fingers at the one with the evil eye, which brought in as well the hanging of horns in private houses, which is still a common custom prevailing today. With apparitions of spirits asking for suffrage it was a different thing. The Church could never pronounce disbelief in apparitions of this kind without contradicting its teaching on the immortality of the soul. Similarily it could not reject the haunting by damned souls without nullifying the solemn prayer for exorcism of evil spirits which had prevailed throughout two thousand years of Christianity. It is for this reason that we find members of the Church getting involved in ghostly manifestations of this kind. Sometimes even in a more spectacular way than seculars, as the dramatic story that follows amply illustrates.

The story which was broadcast on the local radio by Ġużè Diacono, concerns a monk who had for many years patiently assisted a very sick woman. Hers was not some common illness, but a most frightening disease which consumed with excruciating pain, and what was more mortifying was slowly and cruelly disfiguring the woman's face as if the devilish virus that was in her was ensuring that she would never show her face in public again. There was resort to the best medical attention, but one by one the specialists shook their heads. Even if there was to be a cure, which they doubted, there would still be the permanent disfigurement of the face. It was a situation which very often drives one to desperation. But not this woman. When she realised that nothing and no one could aid her she determined to wrest from God the miracle of perfection and began bearing that catastrophe that struck her with the fortitude of resignation trusting only in Him and for Him. Day after day she prayed, lived and prayed in her bedroom comforted spiritually by her faith. Materially, there was the monk who spent long hours with her.

The years flew, but for her they looked longer making her life like a hell on earth to which she was doomed without any hope of remission, and all throughout this time there was only reflected in the woman her total resignation to God's will. To this, the monk was a living witness, being not only her continual companion but also her confessor.

When finally she was on the brink of death there was the natural feeling of sadness in all those around her, but everyone felt that death would for her be a blessing in disguise. Indeed, the monk went further than this in that he was convinced that with her big sacrifice throughout the years of suffering she had earned more than the right to a passage to paradise in the glory of the Lord. More than he could humbly hope to be his lot, when his turn came.

On what was to be her last days with the living the woman was happy. She thanked all that had helped her with the patience and forbearance they had shown throughout her long illness. But her special thanks were for the monk, who after all was not a relative. When she turned to him with tears in her eyes and kissed his hands, she said: "I am afraid that I cannot repay you for what you have done for me."

"It was only my duty," he replied, "and I would do it all over again if I had to."

"Yes, I am sure you would," she said, "but I wish I could have given you something in repayment." Then after a while she continued: "I will certainly pray the good Lord for you when I am with Him in heaven."

The monk did not say anything. Her words had moved him. But they also gave him an idea. It was something that had always troubled him with doubts of the scrupulous which he feared would accompany him to his grave. This woman had suddenly provided him with a solution.

"There is something you can do for me," he told her.

"Yes," she said anxiously, "what is it?"

"There being no doubt that you will be with the Lord when you are gone," he told her, "please ask Him whether I am following His way properly."

She looked at him as if thinking whether he meant what he said, but the anxious look on his face left her in no doubt that he was serious.

"All right, father," she said, "I'll do it for you if it can be done. But how shall I let you know what He says?"

The monk looked at her, and his eyes were shining with determination. His face had gone white with excitement.

"You can give me the reply by coming back," he said in a voice which was now agitated and acute. "On the first night after your death I shall wait for you in my cell. Promise you will do it."

"I will," she replied. That was all they said then.

On the following day she died.

As the determined night approached, the monk could not contain himself. His conscience had worried him with doubts. Now that he was so near to have them resolved he was worried with apprehension. After vespers he hurried to his cell lest his dead penitent would come with the message from the great beyond before time. But by supper time there was neither sound nor movement in his cell. When he retired for the night he took up his breviary and tried to say the office for the day. Had he succeeded it would have been his second saying since he had already said it that day. But he could not concentrate and closed the book again. He had to do something to withhold the suspense that was almost killing him. Never had he thought anyone had had a similar appointment with a ghost, because even though being a saintly one, it was still a ghost. He looked at his watch and found that he had only been half an hour in his cell. It had seemed much longer. There was not a sound to be heard from outside, except the occasional cry of an owl among the silent carobs. In his cell, the only sound was that of his thimping heart. When the clock in the belfry chimed the hour it made him jump. Then he began thinking that after all things might not be so easy on the other side, as he had presumed. But no. In that weak moment this seemed like blasphemy to him.

Then suddenly, before he knew what was happening, there was the apparition. The woman manifested herself. Not in the happy glorious state he had expected, but looking decrepit, forelorn as if she was still suffering. And around her were leaping flames of fire.

The monk was taken aback, and his first reaction was one of horror. He had known that woman inside out for most of her life, and he could not understand. He felt himself crouching back against the headboard of his bed as if to put more distance between him and the dreadful apparition. Sweat was dripping from every pore in his body. Not with the heat of the fire which he could sense, but from the sense of fear that overtook him. Then as if noticing his agony, the ghost of the woman spoke.

"As you can see, father," she said, "I am suffering in purgatory to expiate some minor fault. Please pray for me to hasten my passage to heaven. Only then will I be able to pass your messge, and bring you the reply."

Then she disappeared.

The heavy impression made by that apparition continued to plague the monk throughout most of the night. From the following day he began saying Masses and prayers for the repose of his penitent's soul. But when he wasn't praying his thoughts were on the precise and just ways of God, and of how little man understands them.

He remained pre-occupied until there was the second apparition in the way he had expected it on the first occasion.

This time the woman gave him the answer he wanted.

Chapter 5
Miracles and Devils

Another phenomenon which was once, by all accounts, said to have been very common, but seems scarcely to have occurred in Malta in recent years is the miracle. A likely explanation is that miracles were prevalent when people were more prone to jump to conclusions at a time when imagination, belief and suggestibility were more rife. To-day this is past history, as many wonders which at one time might have qualified to being miraculous have found an answer in an advanced science or an updated knowledge of religion. Much of the rest is known to-day to have belonged to the occult – like the cases in the previous chapter. This is not implying that miracles do no longer occur. Because they do. It is only that man is now more liable to take much less for granted since he is more enlightened to distinguish between what is miraculous and what is not.

As miracles are always involving the religious element it is always necessary to sift out all that which belongs to faith which will leave only the point or points that go to show whether one had a miracle on his hands or some hallucination, or even a belief which had left its mark by time and become unerasable. Far be it from my intention to ignore the hundreds of people who have flocked to venerate the grave lying derelict in the small cemetery of St Lawrence where a 23 year old British marine Thomas McSweeney is buried. He was on 8 June 1837 executed on his ship HMS Rodney for a murder which as it transpired later he might not have committed. There is no doubt that the many who ask for his intercession in whatever favours they seek more often than not get what they want. This can be indicated by the fervour of praying and the burning oil-lamps and candles always found on the grave. But this is normal practice to be expected from people born into a faith which has come down through the ages from the beginning of christianity recognising not only the immortality of the soul but also its existence in a heaven with access to God and His omnipotence. What is not normal, however, is the story that had always flourished of McSweeney's grave lying as it does in a cemetery not generally accessible throughout the year to have a fresh flower placed on it every day by unknown and unseen hands. This is what might have been the miraculous part of this story had it been true. But when I recently went to see for myself there were the oil-lamps and the candles still burning; there were also the dried flowers of many days standing. But there was nothing fresh.

A case which however carried the portent of the miraculous concerned Dun Ġorġ Preċa, a saintly priest who was one day accosted by a young boy pushing an obviously heavy wheel-barrow full of garbage and asked for his help. Without any disdainful thoughts the priest obliged only to have the boy and the wheel-barrow disappear into thin air. He realised it had been no ghost that had accosted him but God who had delineated his mission in life which was to push forward the spreading of christian doctrine which he was then already projecting and indeed finished by doing till the end of his life.

A case which was in its time given the coverage of a miracle but which might have belonged more to the occult was that concerning one Anthony Azzopardi in life nick-named *Ninu Xkora*. The last word meaning a sack was very likely foisted on him because he was always carrying one. Ninu, which is the rural of Anthony, was found guilty of murder and hanged in 1908. His straightforward trial and execution became a posthumous *cause celebre* when it was said that he might have been buried when he was not yet dead. It could have been this that took people to his grave in the Prison cemetery. What is definite is that the first few soon swelled into a crowd praying and asking for his intercession which was evidently forthcoming. Again, this was something to be expected, particularly when it was known that Ninu had died a repentant. The miraculous came later when it was being said that there was the apparition of his ghost in the cemetery which was never verified. There was however the expected climax when a woman who was delayed on her way to the cemetery when taking oil for the lamps on his grave, and finding the gate closed. She was already resigned to turn back when a man she did not know appeared out of nowhere and took the bottle of oil she was carrying. The woman did not think anymore about it until she happened to be shown a picture of the dead man whose grave she had gone to venerate. She had ony one look at the picture. Then she said: "That's him. He was the man who took my oil."

Assuming that the apparition had occurred as stated one fails to see the portentous element always found in a miraculous manifestation. On the other hand there had been a lot of talk of the possibility that Ninu had been buried alive. If this was so then it followed that he had died in his grave very likely with enough emotion to bring an emotive haunting of the place where he is said to have appeared. Could not this have been another case of filling a blank in history through haunting?

The cases of ghosts which make one believe in miracles are legion, and they strengthen the argument why claims for such manifestations are not taken likely. There are factors that can simulate the miraculous, some of them shocking which is tantamount to violation of the holy law behind miracles. This is something which is normally found in places like Brazil where the occult and spiritism have a big say in life. Yet, there was at least one case in Malta which merits a mention in this work.

The beginning was in 1885. On safe and unpeachable ground of a Jesuit house in St Vennera. A young Sicilian novice Alberto Polizzi began showing signs of godliness that were normally attributable to saintliness more than to a simple supernatural origin. As always happens there might have been doubts raised about the visions of God and the Blessed Virgin that he began claiming he was having. Many a smile must have also been raised by the way he described his experiences as if they were things that happened every day. But smiles were wiped out when Polizzi was witnessed by others in a state of ecstatic levitation. This brought the obvious conclusion where it was lacking, and the Jesuits were more than glad and convinced they had a saint amongst them. As if this was not enough to settle any lurking doubts elsewhere there came the day when the young novice was given the stigmata of the crucified Christ. Wounds appeared in his hands and legs, as well as his chest, and all of them as in the case of other stigmatics were bleeding copiously particularly on significant days like Good Friday.

There was no suggestion of any trickery. On the contrary, all who witnessed Polizzi took away impressions of great suffering. Different persons, amongst them clergymen of standing commissioned to investigate from near and far visited the stigmatic and were satisfied that what they saw was of a supernatural cause.

The arguments about stigmata are voluminous and complex, ranging from the hysterical to the impeccable examples the world had to witness in many like Gemma Galgani, Theresa Newman and the incomparable Padre Pio. If there was anything doubtful beneath the armour of obvious genuinity of Polazzi there might have been an open chink in the way he made free with his unique attribute. This did not correspond to the many genuine and devout recipients who would conceal their stigmata or show no outward sign of them so as not to excite the curious. With Polizzi it was not so. Handkerchiefs were often being placed against his chest as if in an attempt to arrest bleeding, but in truth to be kept as a memento. The more so when on being removed there was to be seen on them the facsimile of a heart in blood. Some of these handkerchiefs still exist to-day.

The chink in Polazzi's armour seemed to have opened a little wider when he began to attribute to Divine Providence certain messages and instructions which did not make sense. It began to appear as if there was some conflict going on in his case – between the true and the false; the good and the evil.

When the situation became more disturbing the Vatican was brought in. A specially appointed commission paid a visit to Malta and the saintly novice to study the facts. Those people were not fools. Their verdict was surprising and spectacular. Polizzi was not a fraud, and the stigmata were not doubted to be genuine. But it was declared that they had not been received through divine intervention. On the contrary, they were of a diabolical simulation by the devil.

If there was to be any confirmation that the Vatican's verdict was correct, it came from Polizzi himself who left Malta and the community in 1892, got married and nothing more was heard of him or his stigmata.

Demoniology is another branch of the occult which had as yet not been touched upon. This belief is framed in Spiritism which never found a footing in Malta. On the other hand the devil featured extensively in the local religious field. He tempted and lead one into sin, the preachers said. He also possessed people and premises. Corpses too seem to have been possessed, judging from a report I was given that persons would rather have kept private. It was of a corpse buried in a church which had to be exhumed and exorcised after diabolical interference in the form of cries and screams that interrupted many a church service.

All reported cases of diabolical possession in Malta are always characterised by the sense of fear and reluctance of any would be exorcist because of the devil's inclination to display an intimate knowledge of his life and resorting to proclaim aloud whatever embarassing details in it that he would have preferred to keep private. Maybe this is the reason why little if any of them have come to light. On the other hand what cases of demoniology are recorded in archives carry the element of doubt about their authenticity. It is therefore not surprising that the few cases that have come to light are put down as the product of imagination or folklore. But not all.

Round about the time of Polizzi there was something totally different happening to someone else. The fantastic story first came to light when it was published in Blackwood's Magazine in January 1891, but fortunately enough it had more recently reappeard in a paperback edition by Fontana Books of Lord Halifax's Ghost Book. The author takes the reader back to the time when he was an ensign with his regiment stationed in Malta, and quartered in a barracks situated in a suburb of Valletta. From his descriptions he was referring to Lintorn Barracks which is in Floriana, a town and indeed a suburb of the capital Valletta. The day of the incident being recounted was said to have been Maundy Thursday in late April, but judging from his description of how after crossing Grand Harbour in a *dgħajsa*, the gondola of Malta, from Cottonera to Valletta where he had to thread his way through the crowds thronging Republic Street (then called Strade Reale) watching the solemn procession with the figures symbolizing the Lord's Passion, it must have been Good Friday. Since it is on this day that such a procession is held in Valletta and in many other localities of the island.

He had arrived at his barracks past eleven o'clock with little or no people about at that time of night. Most lights were already out which made the few that were still on in some mess windows more outstanding. Behind one of those windows there was a card game still going on, with one of the participants being a young officer called Ralph who is the subject of this story.

Ralph was a man with an odd history. He was a notorious character among the English residents and garrison, endowed with a certain *diablerie* that stuck at nothing which made him sort of popular with the most daring in society. He was described as dark, with brilliant eyes and black hair; and also a tall lithe figure to match. His smile, when this was put on for the benefit of those he wanted to please was bewitching. He was good at games. Billiards, but more competent in cards. Indeed he excelled in this latter which coud not be described as pastime since it must have got him enough winnings to maintain himself. It could not have been pure skill or luck that was behind this, and there were various whisperings about how this fellow could have had all the material profits of life going always in his direction.

The author continued to say how his attention was

attracted by the two or three persons that were still about in the grounds when he arrived. One of them was a remarkably tall man in a long dark cloak who was standing under the mess window where the card game was still going on inside. He then sauntered into his room, lit a cigar and came out again to find that all loiterers had gone. Except the tall man in the dark cloak who appeared to have not even changed his position. The mess window still aglow, and the sound of voices from inside indicated that the card game was still going on. There was no doubt that Ralph was there and in one of his ravaging moods dominating the scene. Had there been any doubt it would have been settled soon after when his voice amongst the others was heard even from that distance raised as if in some altercation that was going on. There was then some other voice telling him that he had not dealt the ace of spades bringing in Ralph's strident harsh voice to swear that he did, and invoking the Devil to take his body and soul if what he was saying was not the truth.

Hardly had the echo of his last word died down, when the tall cloaked figure who had not moved from his place outside the window made an instantaneous movement. He was seen to leap up with a swift spring on to the window sill and then to disappear into the room from where the swearing had come. In the same instant a piercing scream rang out, and it had the appalling urgency of pain, rage and terror mingled together. Then the tall cloaked man reappeared at the window. But this time he was not alone. Gripped in his arms and half slung over one shoulder there was the recognisable figure of Ralph, struggling desperately.

One moment, the author recounts, he was trying to understand what was going on, as if weighing up whether what he was seeing was really happening, or was it some hallucination; then he collected his bewildered wits and rushed to stop the two men. But the cloaked man was still fantastically quick and agile, even with the struggling figure of Ralph over his shoulder, and before he could be reached had vanished round the corner of the building. The author continued to run but on turning the corner only a few seconds later there was no one to be seen in the barrack square.

The next moment pandemonium broke loose. There was the guard being called out to search the grounds for the two men. At the same time there was someone tearing out from the barracks in search of the regimental surgeon and raising hell with his shouting. The author says how he ran with the crowd that had suddenly assembled to the room where the card game had so dramatically come to an end. There was a table and chairs overturned, and playing cards strewn all over the floor. Half a dozen officers were in a silent group stooping over the prostrate form of Ralph, who notwithstanding his parted lips and staring eyes was stone dead.

In the calm that normally follows such dramatic occurrances what had happened could be laid down in detail. It appeared that the group had been playing *vingt-et-un*, and the game had become tense with stakes running high. A young subaltern had been dealt the ace of spades and stood. But Ralph had then again produced an ace of spades which was too much for the subaltern who had long been noticing Ralph producing such unexpected cards. There was the remonstrance which the author had heard from outside, then those who had been in the group said that there was a momentary gust of air which seemed to shake the window sash, and the card table stirred as if in a slight earthquake shock. Ralph then threw his hands up and fell back in his chair like in a fit, and died. The autopsy held later had indicated he had died of aneurism.

The author could not understand, and for a time he thought that he might have after all imagined the goings he had seen. But there was another man that night who had been looking out of his window and had seen the tall cloaked man in the barrack ground. When he talked to the author days later, he could confirm that what had gone on, he had seen as well.

It became obvious that the devil had answered Ralph's oath and invocation.

Miracles and devils had now suddenly become things of the past. It became conceivable that all might have shared a communal dream filed with fantasies, grotesqueries, evil and inherent irrationalities. But the same could not be said of ghosts. Theirs was a different story which had persisted when other phenomenal manifestations had fallen by the wayside. Now that there was an imminent upheaval in Malta's history it will be worthwhile to see how the island's ghosts were to fare in the new life.

Chapter 6

The Haunted Fifties

Attempts to identify the ghosts of Malta have never been very zealous, and what efforts were ever made to unravel them had always been in the way of conjectures by amateurs. Whatever interest was shown in the subject was more likely because of the close connection there had always existed between ghosts and the local faith of catholicism – something which had indeed always influenced Maltese life. On the other hand the Church never encouraged delving into the occult and the new history that was being made had no plan for ghosts.

Now that Malta was passing through its momentous times of the fifties which can be said to have conceived the nation of to-day, there was little or no time for supernatural trivia. There had already been three elections since the re-establishment of self-government in 1947, with as many political parties taking the reins of power during their respective periods. To occupy Maltese minds there were more important deliberations other than ethereal ghosts. It was felt all round that the time had come to break away from old times which had dragged too long with the Maltese struggling with what destiny seemed to have always allotted them as their lot throughout history. They had always been ruled, with somebody else having the last word in matters which they felt that concerned them. Then the war in which they had given their stupendous contribution had changed all that. In the ten years of its aftermath they had proved to themselves and to the world that they could manage their own affairs. It was then considered only fair to be wanting something more than the self-government they had been given which reserved all that appartained to the island as a fortress to the British Crown.

The government which took over in 1951 had started talks with aspirations for Malta to be given a Dominion Status by transferring responsibility for the island from the Colonial to the Commonwealth Relations Office. But the proposal fizzled out. Another government which assumed power in 1955 then came up with the novel suggestion of integrating Malta with the United Kingdom with its own representatives in the House of Commons at Westminster. Although this proposal received a positive reaction from the British side, it also finished by being strangled by the many knots that were being tied up by the parties concerned in altruistic attempts to safeguard their own interests. The third alternative was one of Independence for which all political parties and also the people behind them were united. The fanfare was sounded and its echoes were to die down only years later after independence was indeed achieved. But in those first years of initiation one had to hope on beginner's luck. The only redeemable asset was that the beginner in this case was a hard worker.

There was also a certain amount of unrest in the first days when the Maltese started on their way to their new coveted ideal. Matters were not improved when the constitution was suspended, and the island reverted back to colonial rule. But now that the die had been cast there was no going back. Changes began to loom ahead. The dockyard was to be handed over to private enterprise after being no longer considered as the potential main bread winner it had always been. A drive was initiated to promote economic development with a view of attracting new industries. Plans for a deep water harbour, industrial estates and re-equipment of the island's electricity supply and other public utilities were put on the drawing board. An Aids to Industry legislation was intimated for enactment which would offer incentives to industrial development. The horse of tourism was also taken out of its stable where it had lain abandoned and forgotten as a potential runner.

This new impetus brought an influx of foreigners to mingle with the Maltese and try to live their life. Instead, more than they learned the local ways, it was for the islanders to be imbued with new ideas and customs which were compared favourably with their ways of living now looking old and backdated. As were also their ghosts.

In those years teeming with change which were hastening social and religious revolutions that were in the offing, the only ghosts that were spoken of openly and without derision were the ideas of Dominion Status and Integration. They had died before being born. Now they were haunting everyone confronted as the island was, by an uncertain future.

As schemes for the new Malta were falling into pattern it was becoming more obvious to the young, and indeed to many of those engaged in founding the new nation that there was neither the time nor the scope for ghosts. Never before then had there been so strong a feeling that ghosts might have after all always belonged to the books of folk-lore as made up fables to boost an uneventful past, or simple hallucinations of the mind. All had heard about them in childhood before the war, the young men were saying, then lived without them during the years of war that followed. But now they could forget them as they looked to the new nation. But, could they?

The curious thing was that notwithstanding the many words being said and new ideas expressed in an endeavour to remove ghosts from the local curriculum as being incongruent with the new life being embarked upon, there seemed to be more than the normal references to them. It was as if the same people who had given the clarion call were – in different terms – still showing affection and emotion towards a not so easily forgotten matter.

Theirs was however only a pragmatism of the times which had very often on previous occasions coloured aspects of Maltese life, only to abate with the first winds of change. On the other end of the spectrum in fact there were those, and they were many, who would not be swayed with the new current because they knew and were convinced of ghosts and their manifestations. Even though they feared them, and had no clue of what lay behind them. Once imbued with knowledge or belief a Maltese is branded for life and carries the stigma with him forever. So much so that notwithstanding the imposed wave of disbelief, there was another wave which perhaps was not as big and noisy, but more persistent and moving consistently to take into every sector of life even in those years of progress, the strange stories of ghosts and hauntings which none could deny or belie.

Pawlu Bugeja was one sunny morning in the fifties on the deck of a ship anchored in harbour. It was one of the many emigrant boats that in those days were too frequently leaving for Australia carrying the thousands in search of a better life in that continent in exchange for the blank void that seemed to be filling the Maltese horizon. Emigration was easy and cheap since it was heavily subsidized by Government. It was the one safety valve for the cauldron boiling with the steam of unemployment alarmingly increasing during that transitional period. There were tears in Pawlu's eyes as he looked over the sea of faces on the quay at Valletta spotted with waving handkerchiefs and filled with the din of words of encourageent and salutation from those who were seeing relatives and friends off. Pawlu could not trace those who had seen him off amongst the multitude of faces. Instead, he tried to formulate his last thoughts of the Malta he knew since childhood and would probably never see again. He had spent all his life in the village of Rabat, which although not visible from the harbour he could visualize perched on a hill and looking so much like a picture from Walt Disney. He was not dwelling on the vista in spring with the galaxy of colours lapping at the feet of shadowed hills. There would probably be something similar in the country he was heading for. But there would certainly not be the same kind of home he had known in Rabat, with all the trimmings that were instrinsically Maltese. Like ghosts, for example.

It's strange how when a Maltese touches upon ghosts there is no swerving from the subject. Rabat was infested with them, Pawlu was thinking. There was a common saying that the *Hares* in Rabat pushes people in cesspits. This was supposed to have been started by those who had been subjected to such ignominy. But if this were some folkloristic anecdote as he imagined it to be, it would still not deflect him from his belief in ghosts, since he had seen some himself. He nostalgically remembered one particular occasion when as a child he had seen a strange woman in his house. Big, dressed and bedecked according to a previous era, she had blocked the door he had to go through. When he had told his parents they had shrugged off his words as childish imagination. When he saw her for the second time he had therefore kept silent. Only however until he happened to see a picture of that woman in the family album and pointed her out to his parents. They were flabbergasted. But so was he when they told him that the woman was his grandmother who had died before he was born.

It was understandable why he could never reconcile himself to what was being said in those days that ghosts did not exist, because he knew they did. Wasn't there the other case he remembered when as a boy he had seen at a friend's house the drawers in a cupboard opening by themselves, and blocking his way every time he wanted to cross the narrow room where he stood? These were things he would remember all his life and carry them with him to wherever he goes as a living memory, however small, of the ghosts of Malta.

As the emigration drive was during the middle fifties gathering momentum, there was those albeit a few who were already returning to Malta after failing to find their feet in Australia or Canada. One day four men with their wives and a couple of children stood on the tarmac at Luqa Airport, looking around at the Malta they had returned to after an absence varying between them from two to four years. One had to do at least two years in the land of his choice if he were to qualify for an assisted passage back. If he did not, then the full fare will have to be paid, and all financial assistance provided to be refunded. Their clothes and smiles at the sun-drenched buildings they must have known so well proclaimed them to all as returned emigrants.

One of them was Joseph Cassar. He had in the first instance found himself jobless after demobilisation. It had not been the end of the world. There were many others like him. But with Joseph it was different. He could not hope for a quick job since he knew no trade that was in demand. All he had done in life before soldiering was making cheese-cakes, a delicacy which all Malta and indeed all who visit her know as *pastizzi*. It was to be expected that they would again be in demand after the war, but Joseph could not wait. He had another problem which concerned something more delicious than cheese-cakes. He had met Carmela in the last months of the war. She was a dark-haired seductive girl with a figure like an hour glass. He had fallen for her like a ton of bricks. They had courted in the little spare time he had, but always under the watchful eyes of her mother. They were never left alone. Maltese protocal of those times would not allow such mesaillance. So rather than waiting for a job to get married, Joseph decided to marry her and emigrate.

But after two years in Australia, Carmela could not stick it any longer, and they returned. Joseph's problems now were to find a job and a place where to live. Both were difficult to find. But his father who had began making cheese-cakes again helped him out by taking him on as an assistant. As for habitation there was none available, unless he wanted a house which was haunted. It was not difficult for Joseph since he had never believed in ghosts. Besides, he would get such a house cheap because of its stigma. The deal was clinched in hushed voices, and he refrained from telling even Carmela of the repuation of the house.

The occurrences began with something mischievous when Joseph heard some noises in an inner room, but on going in to investigate found nothing. Except the cover to a ventilator which he found on the floor. It must have dropped there without anybody noticing. He fixed it in place, only to find it again on the floor on the following day. When this and other similar mischievous deeds continued, Joseph knew that there was indeed something wrong with that house, but kept his mouth shut lest he would alarm Carmela. But unknown to him the ghost or *Hares* had taken a fancy to his wife and was also teasing her in a more docile way. She was as well keeping her mouth shut not to alarm her husband. Then the ghost began making his attentions worthwhile to Carmela by leaving her some money every day. When finally husband and wife learned of the secret that each of them was trying to keep from the other, they laughed about it and said no more.

From this point the story slides into what has become general knowledge. Joseph opened his own business in making and selling *pastizzi* which earned a name for their deliciousness and cheap price. Within a year or two, always in the fifties, people were going to his place from all over Malta to buy them, and no one else in the same line could compete with him. They were really good because I often bought some myself.

What has remained a mystery for many was how Joseph, who had right from the very first said that he intended to make *pastizzi* only until he could find a better job had not only never stopped but increased his business. This too required money, as did the car he was soon running, the way he and his wife dressed and the occasional trips abroad they made. This kind of life was soon calling for a better house in some chic residential quarter. But Joseph and Carmela would not part from their old haunted place, where they still live to-day. It seemed that their comfortable living was tied up more to that house than to anything else.

For every one of the few known cases of those finding money like Joseph Cassar there were many cases of others finding a different kind of enlightenment in the outlook on the occult represented by ghosts. With those who could and would care to do it there was then the comparison being made between ghosts and the most recent scientific inventions that were appearing in Malta for the first time like television. The latter were being looked at as being only developments of principles or natural laws, such as ghosts were being seen as a varnished exhibition of a phenomena that was as old as time. But both sets of principles had always existed. Science and the occult seemed to have always had this in common. They had existed because they must, and not because anybody had proved them as doing so. This must have started the first serious thinking for the identification of ghosts in Malta.

Doctor Frank Busuttil was an eminent Maltese physician. He was highly respected for his integrity. For all I know he might have never believed in ghosts. He must certainly not have had the time to bother about them, being so extensively occupied by his practice. But one day in the early fifties he had an urgent morning call to attend to a young woman who was a guest of an English family in a villa at St Julians. He found the young woman in a hysterical condition and suffering from sever shock. What her hosts could say was that in the early hours of that morning she had rushed into their room screaming like mad and obviously terrified out of her senses. Then she had collapsed in a faint. But he was able to hear the rest of the story from the patient herself after she was restored.

She had been awakened from sleep by a sensation that she was no longer alone, she told him. Then, by the light of her night-lamp she saw a girl standing by the door to her room. She described her well as being dressed in black, and even recognised the Edwardian hair style she was wearing. She asked her who she was but there was no reply. Then she saw her approaching noiselessly.

There had been until then nothing frightening in the approaching girl. There was even a smile on her face, but as she moved closer carrying an air of heavy suspense there was the first realisation that she was not a human being. It was then, when the girl in black tried to touch her that she realised she was a ghost, and jumped out of her bed in panic and ran screaming to her hosts.

It might easily have been the case of a hallucination or a bad dream. But when a Maltese lady, who was a friend of the English family was told of the story she did not think so. She thought she knew the girl who had haunted the house that night, and even produced her picture. The guest had one glance at it and confirmed that the girl in that picture was the same one she had seen in her room. Then the Maltese lady supplied the rest of the story. The girl in black had been the daughter of a Maltese lawyer who had brought sorrow to her family by rejecting her many suitors to become the mistress of an Englishman. The couple had resided in that same villa where she had lead a very lonely life. She had died elsewhere after she was reconciled with her family. But as far as she knew this was the only occasion when she had haunted the house.

There was not a single reason for Doctor Busuttil to doubt this story, and the way in which he had recounted it himself shows that he had not only believed in it but it had also set him thinking.

There were many others that found themselves compelled to give earnest and serious thinking to their belief in ghosts, like Edward for example, a bright upcoming lad for whom phantasmagoria had always been just another fantastic subject like the science fiction he read in his comics. But when in the company of two friends at a catholic centre in Ħamrun he saw a stool moving by itself along a corridor, as if it was being lifted by invisible hands he reversed all his opinions. There was no doubt of what he had seen. His friends saw it too, and when he told his superior about it there were not the words of doubt or disbelief he had expected. Instead, he was told in the most casual way not to tell others about it lest he would alarm them. It was made obvious to him that his superior knew of that regular occurence, which gave it authenticity.

Not even in the remotest village would anyone have dreamed to throw water in the street, in those years of the fifties. It was therefore more senseless than surprising when while going along Tower Road in Sliema, in the part inhabited by the elite Frank X. Darmanin got a douche from a pail of water emptied from a balcony. It all happened in a few seconds. With enough time to hear a window in the balcony open, and for the instinctive raising of the eyes to look up, enough to see a pair of hands emptying the bucket of water which left him no time to dodge its contents. He was suddenly wet all over.

"Hey, what the devil do you think you are doing?" he sputtered, as he saw the window close quickly as it had opened. But there was no reply to his shouting, and he was left shuddering as his anger grew with the ignomony of the situation which made him look like a fool to the crowd that was gathering.

Then the same window re-opened, and this time there was an old lady looking out to see what was causing the commotion. Frank told her, without being complimentary with his speech and exclamations that fell mercilessly from his mouth.

"But you are mistaken," said the woman. "I didn't throw any water. I wouldn't do such a thing. And there is nobody else who could have done it, since there is only my bedridden sister living with me."

Mistaken my foot, thought Frank. How could he have been mistaken. In a flash he thought he would show the old woman his wet state to prove his words. His hand went to his hair which an instant before had been dripping wet. But before he could utter his rejoinder his hands were running over his face, shoulders, and all over his body which had been wet as a sponge. Now he found, he was all dry, as if water had never touched him.

He was suddenly speechless, feeling appalled and ashamed. But he found much food for thought and began to look at the picture of ghosts in a different light.

Police commissioners had always been averse to have the many cases of hauntings in police stations made public. It could have been for this reason that a member of the police force asked me not to mention his name when recounting this story. Norman, as I have chosen to call him was a sane and rational-minded young man. He was a normal person like you and me. Maybe the only difference with him was that he never had any dreams in his sleep. Neither when sleeping at home nor at the various police stations where he took turns to sleep in the course of his duties. There was however, one exception. Whenever he slept at a particular station he always dreamed, and to his amazement he had always the same dream – that of an old woman wearing the dress of a previous era and with a black shawl on her head who would go in his room and throw stones at him as he lay in his bed. She would then always leave the room just before he wakes up.

One night Norman woke up just that little before the usual when the woman had stopped throwing her stones. And he was just in time to see her in person as she left through the door. He rose quickly from his bed and ran after her. But there was nothing and no one in the corridor outside. Nor in any other place in the station.

These were sample cases of persons in whom ghostly manifestations had generated thinking which was lacking in a much bigger sector of the Maltese population long immured with ghostly manifestations, but refraining from exposing them because of the risk of being called mad or superstitious. Either that or these people were just plain terrified. In both cases they were only playing into the hands of the sceptical whose main argument to justify their scepticism was a simple denial of reported hauntings after the war. Their implication was that such reports had only been fables created and believed by a superstitious population in those pre-war days that had since been emancipated and knew better. This was far from being true, because ghostly manifestations continued to feature in Malta, and in the fifties the island was as much haunted as during any other period, before and after.

There was evidence that the new generated thinking about the occult began gaining ground even in those years which was in the way of a first step to verify the ghosts in Malta. But this emerging factor had to contend with a much stronger current which had then began moving down like an avalanche to demolish the old country and raise it up again to the level of modern times that were in the offing. The changes which had been planned some time before were now being implemented. The Admiralty Dockyard changed hands to private enterprise while the swampy lands at Marsa began to receive the first buildings of an industrial estate. Reconstruction was hastened, laying new and modern plans for demolished slums and sites whose only asset when built up had been historical. At the head of this movement there was the British governor, then Sir Robert Laycock, who was being assisted by an advisory board under the chairmanship of Lord Hives, and backed by a five year grant of £29,000,000. The wave of their magic wand set all the planned changes in motion. Harbour, airport, grain silos, fuel tanks, electricity and water supplies. There was also the bait of fiscal incentives set up to attract new industries to the island. Historical buildings long in the possession of private enterprise were retrieved and given a face-lift to provide attraction and knowledge for tourists who were expected to invade Malta and for whom the first hotels began to be built. The blue-print for Malta's change-over from a fortress to an industrialised nation was being put into operation and was leaving no one any option as to where efforts should be directed.

The Maltese played up, notwithstanding the fact that they did not agree with the type of colonial government that was running their affairs. They agreed much less with the new Constitution that was being devised, re-introducing elected representative government, when they had already decided for Independence. But they knew that in their own characteristically astute way, as indeed was always evidenced in their long history of feudalism, they would attain what they wanted. They knew however, and time has since proved them right, that circumstances showed that compliance with what was being laid down for them as being the best road towards their ultimate aim. So in their wisdom they acquiesced to everything and shelved any beliefs they had which did not correspond with the new life they were being led in, until some other time when it would be more opportune to air them. so did those who had been disappointed in their belief in ghosts.

This might have been considered as a small victory by Britain for having after all retained Malta under her wings. Indeed there were already British voices haranguing that the island had lost its one time strategic importance, which was out of context with Russian attitude now characterised by increasing interest in the Mediterranean. When one day fishermen spoke of a ghost ship they had seen whilst returning from their night's fishing it transpired, as the morning mist lifted, that the "ghost" was a Russian cruiser anchored on the shallow shelf off Malta known as Hurd's Bank. Later there were more ships there, destroyers and trawiers, as well as small vessels with strange contraptions which the world later knew as spy-ships. While this was going on British aircraft from Luqa Airfield made the air space over Hurd's Bank their lane; and the flags of six NATO nations, Great Britain, France, Greece, Italy, Turkey and the USA flew from the Headquarters of the Allied Forces, Mediterranean at Floriana. It was history repeating itself, reflecting the time of four centuries back when the flags of the eight langues of the Knights of St John flew over the respective sectors of the island's defences, as a symbol of unity and strength against some common threat.

But if anyone was worried by any threat, it was certainly not the Maltese. Theirs was a different and silent battle that was being fought, in which the current changeover from a fortress to an industrialised country was only the first stage. It was a battle in which they never expected and were not claiming any victories. Those would come later, of this they were convinced.

The only sense of victory that could be felt although not openly evident belonged to those who were openly hinting that the new history that was being made was the epitome of progress because it would remove for ever such customs as bell-ringing, over decoration of churches, legendary ties, fire-works and a hundred other usages that belonged to Malta's heritage. They were the same persons that wanted to ostricise ghosts.

With the winds of change blowing in their favour they could afford to lay it thick, and if there were any misgivings they were all on the other side. Maybe they were all crack-ups, some of these were thinking. Or dangerously retarded people trying to sustain inwardly their old fashioned lives in a time of enormous historical and social change pretending to things that didn't exist. The return on such philosophising was small. What if after all they were wrong? What if it was all make-believe? Failure cast grotesque shadows on their religious beliefs. Yes, even that. Because there was much of what they believed in ghosts that had its feet embedded in the catholic religion. But they needn't have worried because by the same argument of those on the other side it was obvious that assumptions had ran ahead of them.

If theirs had been a battle waged on the subject of ghosts, there had certainly been no victories yet. If there was to be a decisive outcome this would have to come from neither side, but from an independent source having no brief for or against ghosts. Like the new Malta, for example.

This was a decisive time for the ghosts of Malta.

The Inquisitor's Palace in Vittoriosa belonged as the name implies to the first days of the Inquisition when this came to Malta in the fifteenth century and to-day still shines with convincing memorabilia to the powers of the past. There were times when many spoke of its accoutrements particularly its spiked well in which, it was said, the condemned were dropped to rot and die from the wounds inflicted by spikes fixed in the sides to cut into the dropping body. There has never been found any factual evidence of this well of torture, but irrespective of whether this was true or not, the fact remains that the palace had its moments of history.

Fortunately enough, apart from superficial damage this palace survived the wanton bombing of Vittoriosa during the last war. The Dominican Priory close by was not so lucky and was totally destroyed. So when the Dominicans returned to Vittoriosa they were temporarily housed in this palace until their priory could be rebuilt. When the friars left, the palace was restored to its former status of a museum and opened for visitors. It was in fact one of the first places so revived in the new wave of development of a new Malta in the fifties.

By virtue of its background the Inquisitor's Palace was bound to have some ghosts. I heard several stories but I am not in a position to confirm any of them. Besides, its revival came at a time when as has been explained, stories of ghosts were hard to come by because of the truce that seemed to have been enforced.

However, Peter Bugeja, a museum custodian whose duties took him several times to this palace says that he used to hear strange noises which were not attributable to human sources. He was afraid, and always made it a point to stay close to the main entrance where he could be succoured by the presence of people passing by. He went up to the halls on the first floor only in the company of others. Even the locking up he had to see to at the end of day he would do in the company of the last batch of visitors. He thought that this might have been the reason why he never saw any ghosts. But even if he had he would not have said anything for fear of ridicule, being the time when mention of ghosts seemed to have become taboo.

But one morning, an English tourist who had gone into the palace flew back down the stairs in terror. Peter stood petrified looking at him only realising that he was blocking his way out when the man stopped in his tracks panting breathlessly with fright.

"What's wrong?" asked him Peter.

"Wrong?" shouted the Englishman hysterically, "nothing is wrong my friend . . . except that I've just seen a man walking right through a wall."

It was a small matter in a way, but with a lot of significance since it happened to a foreigner who did not know of and had no interest in the truce of compromise that was unintentionally being enforced on ghost manifestations. If his story were to reach the right ears it would notch a point for the existence of ghosts. Truce or no truce. The note of irony to be noted is that the manifestation occurred in the course of one activity just revived in the new wave of development which had by then gathered momentum.

This wave had also reached the airport at Luqa where after turning part of the airfield for use by civil aircraft where a terminal was being built, the Royal Air Force retained the rest for its use. It was obvious that there would be guards posted along the wire fencing that separated the two sections, and it was also expected that RAF police would use dogs on guard duties. They used to roam all over the place with these dogs. But there was one spot where the dogs would not go. Hard as they tried the British RAF police could not control their animals when they approached this spot. The dogs would growl and pull back on their leash as their eyes were fixed in terror on something which couldn't be seen at the spot they feared to thread.

It was the very spot where a British pilot was killed in his plane during the last war. There had been unconfirmed reports of ocular manifestations of the headless pilot. But no one doubted that the dogs were then smelling a ghost. As indeed dogs of the Malta Police still do to-day.

It would have been interesting to know what effects these two occurrances might have had on the sceptics who knew of them, but there was no chance. The hauntings went on without respite. Joseph Zammit-Naro who was running his father's carpentry business housed in the Auberge de Provence in Vittoriosa (they were already advised of eviction to make way for another historical museum) had always expected to see a ghost in that place without ever seeing one. The only ghost he had seen was a spectral form of a man going right through a wooden shelf in a tunnel in Vittoriosa used as an air-raid shelter during the war. It was now that one of his employees ran to him in terror saying that he had "seen something" on the stairs and had apparently walked right through it. Although he did not make it clear what he had actually seen it was taken for granted that the long awaited ghost had finally made an appearance.

Also in Vittoriosa, Maria Darmanin and Assunta Allison were returning home from a late function. It was well past midnight. But it was a pleasant night and they did not mind walking the short distance from where transport had dropped them.

There was a full moon with its light reflected sharp and silvery from the black asphalt road and showing in bright relief the blackthorn blossom stitching a white cotton fringe along their way. Quite close there was St Rocco Cemetery – a small burial place where the dead from the plague of 1813 were buried. Time and a couple of bombs from the last war had rendered it derelict. Only the oil-lamp over the twisted and rusty gate which someone kept attending to, and the few devotees who occasionally went there to pray indicated the place to be a cemetery. Maria was such a devotee, and this might have made her glance in its direction. But if she had intended to say a prayer, it was never utterred. Instead she was choked into silence. Coming through the closed gate of the cemetery she saw a procession of figures wearing the familiar long white habit of an archconfraternity, with their heads covered by a hood in the way of the Klu Klux Klan. Her first obvious thought went to the time of Good Friday when persons so dressed would walk barefooted in the procession and drag chains tied to their feet in penance or a vow. But it was neither the day nor the time for this. Moreover, Maria noticed that the figures were gliding along and not walking. Because they had no feet.

It could have been her imagination, she thought in the stunning terror that had gripped her. Particularly when she glanced back at the hooded figures now to see them disappearing one after the other as they floated right into the bark of a tree. She decided not to say anything about it. But when she reached home her friend Assunta gasped with obvious relief. Then she asked Maria whether she had ntoiced anything "strange" on the way. It soon turned out that she had seen the ghosts too.

Any doubts that both of them might have imagined it all were dispelled in the morning when they found crowds of people in the streets all agog discussing the news of a woman who was taken to hospital during the night suffering from shock after having seen a procession of hooded ghosts going up St Philip Street. It was about the same time that they had seen that same procession. Because it must have been the same one, with the street where it was seen being hardly one mile away from the cemetery as the crow flies. After all buildings would not make ghosts deviate way. I had lived in Vittoriosa all my life but it was only then that my wife began hearing my daughter distinctly calling her when she was not at home. On other occasions she would hear her coming in crying as if hurt, when knowing she was at school. She would still investigate to find neither daughter nor any cause for the crying. My daughter from her part began to hear the beating of a drum in her room, and the opening and closing of the bookcase in my study whenever I was not there. A relative of my wife would not come to my house again after saying that on the first occasion she did, which was at this time, she saw the silhouette of a horse projected on the wall. Everyone was hearing or seeing something except me. Even my younger daughter who was then two years old used to look beyond my wife every time she was in her arms, as if there was someone else attracting her attention from behind.

It had suddenly seemed that the ghosts wherever they happened to be in Malta had decided to break up the truce entered into by the mortals they haunted. The news of the new manifestations that were occurring soon went round the towns and villages. Scoffing unbelievers demanded proof which none was now bothering to give them. There was enough to be found out if one cared to look at ghosts in their true perspective.

But looking in perspective involved knowing scopes and reasons for hauntings. This, none of the haunted knew or cared to find out. Tension was mounting. They were somewhat overjoyed to have had the case of ghosts proven, and yet at the same time they feared them. I would not have been surprised to have learned that this had contributed to the rush for new houses which government began giving out.

In the meantime the sceptics grew quieter. A sly calculation had taken the place of their previous unreasoning stubborness. Some of them were resorting to their last line of defence by the premise that they would still not believe unless they themselves see the manifestations, which of course were not for everybody to see. Others became even more persistent with their enquiries. It was now that there were some interesting codicils.

The Auberge d'Auvergne had been a splended and opulent building in a prominent part of Kingsway (later to be re-named Republic Street) in Valletta. In its time it had been one in the series of notable auberges built by the various langues of the Order of St John linking it with the feudal nobility of the country. In 1930 this auberge was put to the use of housing the Law Courts, and in its basement there was installed the city's police station. Since then and until it had to be abandoned after it was severely damaged by bombardments during the last war, it had been common knowledge that the place was haunted by a monk.

There were many reliable people involved and who could vouch for the strange manifestations that occurred in the building, particularly that part housing the police station and the prisoners' cells. Amongst these there was the Superintendent of Police who was once tugged violently out of bed while sleeping there. There was also the inspector who often heard noises of jangling chains whenever he lay down on his bed, with the noises stopping as soon as he rose up. To many other members of the police the haunting ghost manifested itself and they all agreed it was a monk they saw, who would always choose the early hours of the morning for his earthly sorties all of which being characterised by the well known spell of coldness. But the most remembered occurrance concerned an inspector who after hearing a tramp he had locked up in a cell for the night shouting with fear, went down to investigate. On his failing to return, other policemen went down to look for him and he was found lying prone in a corner, petrified and shaking in a terrible state of shock. When he was helped back and regained his composure he recounted how he had seen the monk approaching him on going down to the cells. Then before he knew it he had passed right through him which made him experience a sensation of clammy cold. Then he had fainted.

All this was witnessed and confirmed by the vagrant who was in the cell.

Since the building was vacated all this was forgotten. It was only remembered now when the Auberge d'Auvergne came to be reconstructed. In a part of the basement which had remained standing, a walled up door was found. When the blocking stones were removed, giving access to a cell-like recess, some human bones were found with the dust inside. It was very likely that they were the remains of some individual who had fallen foul of some Knight of Auvergne. It was even more likely that this might have been a monk since walling up a person alive was even in Britain in the times in question, a common method of punishing defaulting monks.

Coming at the time it did, this discovery could not fail to have an impact on the many dubious and anxious minds. It provided a cause and scope for the haunting, and was in a way a clue towards explanation of the many other cases many were now thinking about. To increase their fervour there was the timely recollection of a more interesting occurrance of some years back which public opinion had relegated to folk-lore. It concerned the 367 year old cemetery of St Leonard lying on the outskirts of the village of Żurrieq where at one time horses would shy violently rather than go past the cemetery. There had by then already been a legendary story of a beautiful young woman who would accost people passing that way and invite them to pray and ask for favours from the dead buried there, since they were all in heaven and in a position to grant their requests. But there was later something more sinister which was making the horses act as they were doing. It materialised in the form of a spectral figure of a man who appeared to a farmer on his way to the market with his horse and cart. On the first occasion the farmer turned back hastily and returned home. But when again there was the same apparition he had recourse to a priest from Żurrieq who was known for his godliness. When for the third time the farmer was confronted by the ghost, there was the priest with him who dismounted from the cart and approached the spectre.

What passed between human and spirit in that exorcising contact no one knew. But on the priest's instructions the police later unearthed a skeleton of a man from that road. It was then given christian burial, and since then there had never been any more apparitions.

Seen in the light of the find at the Auberge d'Auvergne this story bore the look of authenticity. It was further being deduced that this ghost had not only haunted in search of a proper burial but had probably uncovered his murder.

But even if its detials had been lost in the passage of time there had been another occasion in 1941 which many remembered and now revived as the incidence of haunting by the murdered was being raised. This was something which happened at a place called St Paul's Steps. This will not be found so described on any map, being as it was even then before 1940 only a small hamlet on a windswept hill overlooking the glorious vineyards of Bur-Marrad and further down the enchanting Salina Bay. According to the legend it was at this place that St Paul had been entertained by the Maltese following his prodigious shipwreck in 52 BC bringing Christianity to Malta. Hence its name. If St Paul's shipwreck had had such a momentous effect on Malta and the Maltese his brief sojourn at this place which was to bear his name had certainly left no impact on the spot. There is still a small chapel but nothing more except fields and a row of houses which was never finished to make a street. Two of these houses had for years been abandoned and given a wide berth by the few inhabitants because they were haunted.

When they were still inhabited there had been nights when they were disturbed by noise and clamour that came from nowhere, as if some boisterous party was going on from midnight to dawn in both premises. Until one day, the respective inhabitants being aware only of the din in the other's house and not in their own, taxed each other with the unseemly noise. Both pleaded innocence, and indeed a conjoint search brought no result. There was nothing and no one found inside to produce that noisy revelling. yet, hardly had the menfolk joined their waiting wives that the din began again, and continued until both families fled in terror.

No one had gone near those houses – until 1941 when one of them was hit by a bomb and in a walled up spiral staircase which was now exposed there could be seen the still clothed remains of a known village Play Boy who had in his time sown many wild oats. But whose sister had been the mother of one of the families who had lived in those houses.

After the remains were removed the haunting stopped altogether.

The interesting case which emerged now as if to consolidate all that was building up in overtones of dread concerned a brighter landscape which made it sound less oppressive. It concerned the village of Lija, unalloyed and unmodified by modern trends, and as it had always been in the past still known for its orange groves and orchards as endowed by nature, and mangnificent fire-works that are made by man. The protagonist house had been considered a decent building for its times of a hundred years back. It was in a street made up of mixed old and new buildings starting from the square lying in the shadow of its prominent church and going to the periphery and wrong side of the village.

It wasn't a street like others. Bright where it should have been dull and with a clean look rather than shabby. This might have been that gave it the title of avenue. There were none the less some drab houses and balconies with windows like rheumy old eyes. It was however quiet, like all the streets in Lija. Those who remembered the house said that it was a two storied building in faded stone coloured lime-wash, and tight lipped windows. And that it was haunted.

This seemed to coincide with the finding of two skeletons when the remnants of the house, after it had been badly hit by bombs during the war, came to be demolished to make way for reconstruction. But when it came to expressing one's self on the possible identity of the persons whose remains were found, there was a blanket of silence.

Some silences however are louder than a scream. It soon became public knowledge how a long dead police officer who had at one time lived in that house was in the habit of interviewing foreign variety artistes arriving in Malta there before they would be granted a permit to stay and perform. Two of these had never left the island. Now, as a possible explanation, there were the two skeletons found, which had belonged to females. Conclusions about the hauntings were suddenly being reached in silence. What was being unsaid however became louder and clearer than a parade ground order.

To the now eager minds there seemed to be no more doubts. In the same way that good spirits could return with their requests for suffrage, and of this there had never been any doubt, so could others function within limitation. Truly enough there was much that was still not understood, and many senseless stories stood to be classified. But now there was no time for post-mortems. The new life was rushing in and overtaking all and everything. The schemes which had been gathering momentum were now fully geared up with an obvious promise of economic advance in the approaching sixties. The 1959 Constitution came into operation with forecasts of years of prosperity and new hopes. To see all this through Sir Guy Grantham took over the reins of governorship. He was the first Naval Officer to administer Malta since the death of Sir Alexander Ball in 1809.

Like him too he played a prominent part in taking the island into an era of organisation and plenty. And with the many innovations being laid down to lift the island with the modern nations there were no nuances raised or mentioned. So, while the buildings for factories and hotels were going up, the Maltese built their churches; with the night spots sprouting up to entertain tourists there were still the festas with their processions and loud fire-works. In the streets there were the first enterpreneurs driving their Mercedes and already looking like overnight lords within a stone's throw of festering slums, disease, shouting children and beggars, with the din of pealing bells. It was a life being maintained neither from necessity nor from lack of knowledge of better things. It was the local life, blending the old with the new as if all were hesitating to discard the well-tried methods of living for the modern ways that were being hustled in.

There were also the ghosts which for a time had seemed to have lain dormant until Malta could breath again, and had recently returned as if to have a place in any future Maltese life.

The truth was that they had never departed from it, and would retain their place in it for ever.

Chapter 7
Patterns of the Sixties

The sixties brought an overnight change in Malta. With the opening of doors for expertise, industrialists and other types considered necessary for the intended progress, and yet so short in the island, there was an immediate and steady flow of foreigners, mostly British, Engineers, architects, accountants, chefs, businessmen and a host of different technicians. All of them were on a temporary permit, tailored to give them time and chance to train local counterparts. Malta had suddenly become an island of temporaries, a place of just-arrivals and only visitings built on the shifting sands of progress. There were also the servicemen – belonging to the Royal Navy, the Army and Royal Air Force, as part of the British garrison and also those attached to NATO Headquarters. All of them had a job to carry out, but there were those who did more than that. They loved, married, settled down and began to raise families. Meanwhile, the promised self-government materialised and in 1962 there was the first elected Maltese government under the new Constitution drafted by Sir Hilary Blood. The governor Sir Guy Grantham was followed by Sir Maurice Dorman.

This immigration provided new ties and contacts. For the second time within a score of years there came a change to Maltese life. The first occasion had been during the war when the Maltese who had lived, fought, suffered and died with the British in defence of their country and freedom had perforce to become imbued with British customs and philosophies. Now something similar was happening.

In the same way that both established and upcoming local businessmen learned of the importance of having a private secretary, so the girls aspiring to this post became at home with what it entailed. There were new definitions being found for engineers, town-planners, business managers and hoteliers. For the first time there were even *ad hoc* courses of study introduced in the newly built Polytechnic. Now the Maltese learned of the tycoon, and having no synonym in their own tongue adopted the word. They did the same with boom, crane, night-club, show, typing and casino. In the same way British counterparts quickly adopted Maltese words which had no concise meaning in English like for example *lawdemju*, a word describing the payment to be made by a purchaser of land to the first original seller. The local women too became suddenly aware of what was permissible for them in behaviour which had before been taboo. Skirts became higher, and for the first time bikinis made an appearance on the beaches, notwithstanding the sharp retorts of the church.

There were only two matters in which the Maltese resisted British influence and refused to give an inch of their own ground. One was religion, which had remained unasssailed and unchanged since its inception with St Paul's momentous shipwreck in 52 BC. The other was the knowledge and belief in ghosts.

It was realised that even if not as old as their own the British had a similrily interesting ghost heritage which had a lot in common with local beliefs. But there was much in their stories that invited doubt and disbelief. They knew as they could now also confirm from British settlers and their books about the possibility of certain emotional acts to impinge themselves in life after death, but they failed to understand and much less to believe that this could produce headless horsemen, phantom carriages, ghostly armies and the like with which the history of ghosts in Britain was riddled. It was admitted that these were thrilling tales, but they were also unconvincing. They invited stronger scepticism which Maltese believers were trying to resist. So rather than reviving the case for ghosts in Malta, as some would have it, this British influence was threatening to debunk it.

There was however room for comprisons to be made. The locals were quick to learn of the many manors and houses in Britain lying dead and ininhabited, yet open to inspection for their legendary haunting. In Malta, similarily haunted houses were in the majority still garnished, lived in and evidencing twentieth century ghosts. They were far from being legendary. Many British tales were exaggerated and offering no scope for the haunting and much less the means of verification. Much of what the Maltese had lived with for ages in the way of the occult was still with them to be heard, seen and verified. It soon became the general opinion that British interest in psychic phenomena was utterly detached from the scientific point of view and was therefore miles apart from local interests and Maltese determination to remain absolutely objective. The word went round that British ghost stories were only intended to raise the value of property. As if to confirm this there was the comparison being made between the locals who were still terrified of their ghosts, and the average British resident who seemed to languish after the possibility of living in a haunted house.

As was to be expected there were many to take advantage of this. Dun Martin, a scrupulous Gozitan priest had decided to sell a house he had in Gozo. It had remained uninhabited and unwanted for many years because of its reputation of being haunted. With the coming of the building boom he had his only chance to get a reasonable price for it, with no question asked. The crazy British residents would go for anything and pay abnormal prices But it was another Gozitan like him who wanted to buy the house. He was a sprightly astute contractor who knew how to make a good deal. He offered £4,000 for the house, and the priest agreed. He had expected much less. So much so that by the time of the conclusion of the deal he was having a crisis of conscience thinking that after all he should have told the buyer of the house's reputation which devalued it. He found a way out of the crisis by deciding to tell the prospective buyer everything before he would have him sign the contract. Even at the risk of losing the providential sale. He would not burn himself in hell. Not even for £4,000.

As things were he needn't have worried because the buyer had already found a British purchaser for the house who was ready to pay him £6,000. When the deal came to be concluded the priest told the contractor everything.

"Is that so?" said the astute man feigning surprise.

"Yes," said Dun Martin, "do you still want the house?"

"Yes, I do," the other replied. "But you must now reduce the price agreed upon since the house is haunted."

"Oh yes, I will," said the relieved priest. "You can have it for £3,000. Is it all right?"

Of course it was all right. The contractor bought the house, and the following week sold it to his British buyer. As the priest had done he also placed his cards on the table with his client, and told him that the house had a ghost. Because of this he asked for an additional £1,000 over the agreed price, and the client obliged.

I never managed to find out whether there had indeed been any ghosts in that house. But there had certainly been many houses sold at good prices because they were reputed to be haunted. The buyers were of course always British. Even so, many more houses which had lain closed and derelict for many years were not sought. They remained abandoned till this very day.

One point which clinched some equivalence with Maltese ghosts and provided common ground for comparison was the belief where this was forthcoming that some ghosts were spirits form another existence. But while Maltese beliefs were closely connected with their religion in that such spirits being of the departed and were in heaven, hell or purgatory, British theories and usages here provoked the stirrings of doubts and disbelief with the practice of seances in the way of a hot line to the other world which more often than not produced fakes and shamen. In Maltese eyes this was making fun of the supernatural, and seances were then considered taboo in Malta, as in fact they are still to-day, twenty years after. Contrary to what might be the impression, Maltese superstition has never gone as far as having any chants sung, or the beating of drums. Nor has there ever been any established ritual to be practised for the communication with spirits in another world. Spiritism has never been known to have been practised. Even the mention of the word is not looked at with benign eyes.

It was therefore not in the least for fetched for anyone to think, after comparison with the vaster and less stable story of British ghosts, that the Maltese theory was as true as it was simple, and very likely in a class of its own.

What strikes a postive note here is the fact that all this was happening at a time when none knew of the research and string of experiments that were then already being carried out by Dr Raymond Moody in the United States on which he later based his books "Life after Life" and "Reflections on Life After Life." From investigations carried out with people who had clinically died but were resuscitated back to life Dr Moody could ten years later formulate a picture of the spirit state in another existence. He wrote amongst other things of a realm of bewildered spirits most of whom are continuously unsuccessfully trying to communicate with persons till physically alive. It appears that the general characteristic attributed to spirits is that they are unable to make themselves visible and much less to communicate with humans. However, there may be rare occasions when through some effort, freak or a wave of unexpected energy they might become visible but are still unable to communicate. If and when in some rare case they do manage to communicate it is always in a one way direction and with great difficulty.

This is all surmise, intelligent guessing, if you will. But it is all fantastically reflected in several manifestations. I was convinced of the basic truth behind Dr Moody's writings because I myself found out persons during my research who could describe something of the after-death state after they had been resuscitated from clinical death. As for the other characteristics of spirits Saviour Sacco assured me that after a friend of his had died in hospital, he met him again in his home in spirit form flitting up the stairs (without any visible feet) as if in an attempt to meet him and speak, which of course he could not do. For all I know the rare and limited ability of spirits to communicate in a one way direction may be reflected in cases of premonitory ghosts. I know of a well known Maltese family who on three consecutive occasions was warned beforehand of a death in the family which always occurred with deadly precision. I have also come across the case of a mother and her children who some time after the death of the husband and father began to hear him calling the mother during the night. It was no case of imagination. All of them heard him and recognised his voice. They began to call him back themselves and ask him what he wanted. But there was no reply. A month later the mother died. He was never heard calling her again.

How could one explain that two of my brothers-in-law had an almost identical re-action of what they consider to have been a supernatural occurrance, at the same time and while they were in their own respective homes? One of them was asleep and felt something or someone wake him up. The other was at that same time watching television when he felt an invisible presence flitting past him. The first one thought of his mother who was sick in hospital, and stopped there. The second one had also the same thought, but took up the telephone and rang up the hospital. It was confirmed to him that his mother had just died . . . right at the time he and his brother living away from him, had felt her presence.

These were all flashes of supernatural phenomena coming in without any reasonable explanation but none the less providing bits of evidence for an uncomplicated Maltese theory that has never been challenged or shaken. Now, in the sixties, with Malta riding the waves of progress and rushing abreast with other nations in the fast race of life it was considered to be past sticking to old theories that had been proved, packed and done away with. Such as the case for spirits from another world. There was nothing more to be said on that. There were other phenomena to be looked into. There had also been the theory concerning ghosts manifesting themselves through impinging their last moment of high emotion just before their death. There had also been enough indications to satisfy Maltese belief in this as well, even though the solution kept eluding everyone. But there were also now being put forward new British theories which did not correspond. One such theory which was to persist even later, attributed ghostly apparitions to the atoms of ectoplasm that might have been taken by the spirit when separating from the body which might have been polarized and might have produced the apparition. It was at that time a too cumbersome theory, full of so many mights, on something which had happened and gone and could not be verified. Maltese response was simple and without any circumlocutions. Their theory was based on what could be seen from manifestations that were going on in the sixties. They would if they could go deeper, but it had to be the ghosts to come to their help with two magnificent cases. The first providing much food for thought and reflection, and the other to carry on the way of ghosts when the tendency was to debunk them.

Ironically enough there had to be an English woman involved in the first case, whom I am calling Mary Marvin. When Mary succumbed to the charms of her Maltese boy-friend little did she think what she was in for. She could not ask her lover home because of her husband. So she readily agreed to go with him somewhere which was secluded. Reggie, as I am calling him, had already thought of a spot. In the way of a starter to their amorous adventure there were a couple of drinks at the Buskett Road House, the imposing public house cum restaurant and night spot that had newly opened as one of the first of a series of tourist attractions. It is a very nice place during the day, surrounded as it is with deep valleys, hills and the greenery of Buskett Gardens. But now it was dark, and raining cats and dogs. The only attraction for the lovers was each other's company and the passion that was burning inside them.

At eleven it was time to go. They drove to the selected spot which was really only round the corner a hundred yards or so away, beneath the towering walls of Verdala Castle, the haunt of the Blue Lady. Neither of them knew of the story. I suppose it would still not have made any difference had they did, with both of them being sceptics and the state they were in. But apart from their feelings it was an eerie spot they had chosen.

The rain did not look like stopping, and flashes of lightning were becoming more frequent showing in day brightness the deserted road with no other building in sight other than the haunted castle. The only sound other than that of pouring water was of rolling thunder. In between there would be the scrambling noise of some rodent making a hurried change of position in the shrubbery to escape the rain, as if emphasizing it was no night for animals, and much less for humans.

Reggie was damning his bad luck for having picked on such a night for his escapade. For all he knew, Mary might have been doing the same as she had not said a word since they had parked beneath some trees. But he was wrong. The moment he turned to her as if to see whether she wanted to go on, she went to his arms and he was covering her face with hungry kisses. It was then that there was the sudden cracking flash of lightning throwing the asphalt road again in bright light as that of a hundred magnesium flares. Reggie could not help turning his face momentarily to the road with the flash to be suddenly stricken with boundless terror.

In that brief moment of light he had seen crossing the road and going towards them a procession of hooded figures, wearing the well-known white habit of the archiconfraternity that has already been mentioned elsewhere. They only differed from the Klu Klux Klan by the rosary chaplet of black beads which he saw hanging from their waist. For a few seconds that looked like minutes he stood there, stuck to his seat as if petrified into immobilisation. He was hoping it had all been his immagination and was hoping for another flash of lightning which would show him that he had been wrong. In the meantime he did not want to say anything to the woman beside him not to alarm her. But at that very moment he felt her warm body going deadly cold, and there was also the shuddering which was an indication that she must have also seen the spectres.

There was then another cracking flash, and this time both of them had their eyes on the road. The spectres were still there in procession, now seen more distinctly.

Because they were closer. Then Mary began to scream.

Without another thought Reggie started the car and throwing all caution to the wind drove away as if the devil himself was on his tail. He did not stop until he saw Mary home.

This was the third confirmed case of the apparition of such ghostly procession. The other two had been in Vittoriosa and the eye witnesses who had recounted them to me had never bothered any further about them. With Reggie it was different. What's more, he was living in a different time when people wanted to know all about what was happening in their new fast moving life. And this included ghosts. He had never believed in them; but now he had seen them for himself. None would dare and tell him he had imagined things. Besides there was Mary to corroborate and describe those moments of the apparition as the most terrifying of her life.

This time too it was Reggie who began probing and pressing for the explanation which was not readily available. It was indeed his sense of observation tht provided what could have been a clue, when he mentioned the possibility that the ghosts were also wearing a hat.

"But you said they wore a hood" he was told.

"They did indeed wear a hood," he replied. "There is no doubt about that. But they could have also worn hats, with their brims turned upwards. Although it is difficult to say since it must have also been a white hat." Then after a moment of concentration he continued, "Yes, I believe there was a hat."

As he said his last words something clicked, and a colourful episode of Maltese social history emerged. There had been only the Archiconfraternity of the Holy Rosary whose members wore the long white habit with hood and hat. Because of its acts of mercy this body of men was also known as the "Societas Misericordiae" (Society of Mercy). It was instituted in 1575 with the approval of the Holy See, and having besides its duty of promulgating and encouraging the recitation of the Holy Rosary, a secondary commitment of promoting spiritual and material welfare of prisoners. But with particular attention to those condemned to death.

That this society was very popular can be seen from

the fact that since its institution there had been many prominent citizens who joined its ranks. In their time there were many Knights of St John amongst its active members; there had been also two grandmasters – Manoel Pinto de Fonceca (1741 – 1773) and Emanuel de Rohan Polduc (1775 – 1797) who were its rectors during their reign. To this very day the society can boast of having on its books members of the clergy, men from the legal and medical professions, the civil service and others from the higher echelons of society. But the most significant point in its existence must have been the function it undertook to attend to those condemned to the penalty of death. Gruesome as it may appear this duty had always been its most colourful and traditional activity throughout the last four hundred years.

On being notified of an impending execution, the members of this society would be assigned a town or village for the collection of funds to go towards the material and spiritual help of the condemned person. They would leave out only the places where the crime was committed and where the prisoner's family resided. But their duty did not end there. After the collected funds would be disposed of, with one half going to the prisoner's family, and the other half being given in alms to the Dominican Fathers for the celebration of Masses for the repose of the soul of the condemned person, they would turn their attention to the prisoner. Six ecclesiastical members of the society, known for their duty as *Confortatori* meaning Comforters, would provide spiritual comfort to the prisoner during the three days preceding the execution. On the appointed day then, the members would attend Mass at the Prison Chapel where the prisoner would be invited, as he is entitled by the society's regulations, to become a member of the society. Their last duty would then be the solemn burial service at the Prison Cemetery.

Until the year of the last execution in Malta which was in 1943, the white hooded figures of the *Misericordia* had become a traditional sight, and the interest they created was enhanced by the fact that their appearance had always been rare because of the low incidence of crimes meriting the capital punishment. It was a sight which in its time was wrought with awe and apprehension – when it belonged to humans, because it signified death. When it belonged to ghosts it was bound to strike terror in the boldest of hearts.

One cannot help wonder as to what awesome reason must have been behind those apparitions, but it was certain that the people who witnessed them had nothing to do with it. They never knew of that arch-confraternity. This rules out any possibility of the British theory. On the other hand it was more likely that the ghosts might have been repeating some action – one which had been charged with emotion – which had engaged them in real life. Working on such a premise one cannot ignore the point that many of the condemned became members of the society at a time when they were under stress and maximum emotion – just before being killed. Another point to be considered is that a mile or two away in the direction the procession was moving there lies Verdala Palace (not to be mixed with Verdala Castle) just past the main entrance of Mdina, which was in the fifteenth century the Court of Justice and a place of execution to where the members of the society must have been very often in their relevant times to assist some poor person before his approaching death.

But if Reggie could believe how the apparition had like many others repeated something from the past, bringing back a living element of the country's social history he was at a loss to understand how it could have been brought about.

Indeed, reflecting about it, one cannot help recall a suggestion made by Margaret Murray in her book "My First Hundred Years" where she attributed such pattern hauntings to a form of photography. Her suggestion was based on the assumption that a combination of light and constituents in the air similar to those used in photography might make an imprint of any figure or action as any camera catches a subject. Then in the same way as the prepared surface in a film on which light waves are recorded remains blank until developed, so will ghostly apparitions "photographed" in their own time disappear until there are applied the right conditions of light, cosmic rays, X-Rays, neon, etc . . . which are known to be contained in lightning as in other natural elements. Margaret Murray supported her theory by certain points such as that ghosts always appear in a restricted area suggestive of the place and time when they are photographed, and are always clothed in the same garments also suggestive of the time and occasion of their origin. She calls on other supporting points such as the cessation of hauntings attributable to imprints fading in the course of time like a photograph, and the occasional reappearance in exceptional atmospheric conditions, like the ones prevailing in the case just mentioned.

It must be said that there is some sense in such a theory, and if there was to be any forthcoming proof of this phenomenon, then the possibility of such photographed ghostly figures fading out by time could provide the answer to the many headless or limbless ghosts which feature in British phantom fantasy. What would be easier for a photographed ghost to have the part where his head appears fade before the rest and leaving him headless in the photograph? On the other hand this theory cannot explain ghosts which move about and the noise they make, whatever it might be. There are also ghosts which appear indoors, or even in the open when they are certainly not exposed to the light, rays and other sources of energy which were so handy for the brothers of the *Misericordia*. The next case is in fact an example of such a haunting being completely sterile of the mentioned conditions.

It happened in a house in a fairly modern quarter of Sliema. The town itself is modern and not where one would expect to find haunted houses. Harry and his wife Tessie had certainly never entertained any thoughts of the kind.

One night after he had retired to bed, Harry was alarmed to hear a noise downstairs. "It sounded," he said, "like the regular footsteps of a man walking on the tiled floor with a crunching noise as if he wore sandals." His first thought was that his wife might have failed to lock the door and someone had walked in. But when he asked her she said that the door had been locked. Then calmly she told him not to worry and go back to sleep. But he wouldn't. Instead he got up to investigate. Nothing and no one was found that could have made that noise. And the door was bolted as his wife had said.

The noise had stopped while Harry was downstairs. Silence had then accompanied him as he walked back upstairs to bed making him think that he might have imagined it all. But hardly had he got beneath the blankets when the noise started again.

Harry had never believed in ghosts, and even at that very moment he was trying to find some rational explanation for the phenomenon. More particularly when he could see that his wife was not at all troubled, and was indeed inclined to make light of the disturbance.

But when night after night the same disturbance came on again and persisted he could no longer take it lightly. On some nights there was a variation in that the footsteps would be heard coming up the stairs and go past the bedroom door to fade away. He would remain awake sensing the new atmosphere that began to prevail around him and force the fact upon him that the house was haunted. When he could not escape the issue he became restive. Not only at night, but every time he was at home. He began to avoid being alone, and would jump at every unusual sound. For the first time in his life he was afraid. He realised too that he was now believing in ghosts.

His wife did not seem to be unduly perturbed. But she now began to take it upon herself to wake up whenever there was the noise as if not to let him face it alone. To use Harry's words, "it wouldn't be true to say this happened every night, but it went on for a long time, and did not miss many nights."

In his attempts to think of a possible reason for the haunting, hoping for a similarily possible relief, Harry found out that there had been a time when the administrator of that house who was a priest had refused rent when his wife's family had lived there before he got married. In his converted state of belief he thought of a possible clue. If the rent had been pledged for any Masses to be said – and the priest had refused rent – Masses were not being said – and some suffering spirit might be chasing his due. It was not hard to persuade his mother-in-law to pay all the rent due in one go. She had it put aside for the day when she knew it would have to be paid. But the administering priest had died, and Harry, now more convinced that he had found the clue went to his substitute who was a public notary.

There was however no record of any money being due. Still, Harry insisted on paying. He was now a terrified man. "I think you are being stupid," said the notary, and in his tone there was the sarcasm of a young man and a sceptic. It was the attitude of the young generation of the times. Harry was not old and belonged to the same generation. But he had heard the ghost and believed it existed. It was a situation reflecting the division of the Maltese in two sets of opinion about ghosts – being so closely near, and yet so far.

For some nights after the money was paid the noise was not heard. Harry thought that the restless spirit had been placated. But suddenly it came back to harass him again. But not his wife.

One day he returned home as usual. a young niece who was staying with them on that day ran to him saying how in the morning she had mistaken somebody else for him in the house.

"Who was this that you mistook for me?" he asked her, trying not to show the anxiety that had suddenly assailed him.

"It was a man who had walked in while I was in the yard with aunt Tessie. I told her it must be you, but she said it wasn't."

He knew now there must have been something abnormal going on, and in his inner self thought that the ghost might have had something to do with it.

"But what kind of man was he?" he asked her again. "Can you describe him?"

"No," said the child, because when I ran to meet him thinking it was you he had already walked upstairs."

So he had gone his usual way, thought Harry. Then he put another question: "How did you know it was a man, if you didn't see him?"

"Because when I went back to the yard I happened to look up and saw him looking at us from the roof. auntie saw him too."

"No, I didn't," said Tessie who had now joined them.

Harry stood looking at her not understanding what

was going on. But after she had sent the child away, she said: "The child was right, Harry. But I did not want her to know the truth. There was a man who came in and went up to the roof. She saw him looking down at us. And so did I. As I had in fact seen him do on other occasions."

Tessie's statement confirmed all that Harry had been thinking. It also explained her calm attitude during the manifestations they had experienced. Now, instead of the expected fear he had a new feeling inside him. Like an innermost sensation that he was on to something new and exciting, but not being quite sure what.

"I suppose it was him . . . the ghost," he said.

"Yes," said Tessie, "it was him." Then she continued to describe him as being middle-aged in appearance, quiet looking and dressed in the tell-tale flannel vest with a blue lining on the neck line, and tattered trousers of no particular colour. On his feet he wore sandals.

"Do you know that you are describing a mason?" said Harry.

"Yes," replied Tessie, "that is the impression I got from the very first time I saw him."

Even though he had never dabbled in the occult Harry felt at once that he was facing something which could be checked. Some theory that could be proved to be factual, and would help him and others. He realised his luck in that his first contact with a ghost had not come expressed in unreadable language or some illogical manifestation which found no explained solution. Without knowing it he was outlining the simple way of learning about ghosts by throwing aside all scientific caution and crash the barrier to reach to the obvious and logical if this could be found.

But fortunately it was not difficult. It was found out that when some reconstruction work was being carried out in that house some years before, a mason answering to the description of the ghost fell to his death from the roof into the yard. The identity of the mason concerned was also established and no one then seemed to have any doubt that in going up to the roof and looking down at the yard the ghost must have been reacting his last emotional moments in life, which had become a pattern haunting.

The explanation as far as this type of haunting was concerned was satisfactory. But imagination had to be stretched further if one were to form some theory of how it could have come about. As in the case of other indoor hauntings there had been neither conditions to be applied nor any prepared ground to receive them. Yet the ghost moved about to be seen and also heard which indicated the presence of some energy. This was no mean matter since the energy sometimes demonstrated by some manifestations is more than one would normally expect from a living human being. One could not however ignore the fact that the indicated use of energy also implied a manipulator. Energy would not function by itself in the same way that a manipulator would not operate without it. There had to be the two elements, and which must in some way be connected. If it was therefore difficult to find the source and kind of energy it was obvious tht investigating minds would turn to the manipulators which were the ghosts.

It might have appeared that a stage was reached with investigating minds when ghosts and energy were running into a vicious circle. One could only break away from this by delving further into other psychic phenomena which were known to be abundant in the local scene, although unexplored and undiscussed. Astral projection was one of them. And there was much to be deduced from this phenomenon which began to come into the open just about at this same time as Malta was becoming more inquisitive of her ghosts.

Chapter 8

The Case for Incongruous Hauntings

Anyone listening to Joseph Chetcuti recounting his experiences of astral projection might have taken him for a lunatic. But he was nothing of the sort. His first experience had come about when one day being dog tired after working in his mother's garden he lay down on the bed to rest. Suddenly he began to leave his body without any effort whatsoever, and found himself in a translucent spiritual form floating all over the room and the bed where he could still see his physical body lying there. Having already read about this phenomenon he was not surpised, but rather enjoyed the experience until he returned to his body. He was averse to talk about it, until he had his second and more definitive experience when he was involved in a traffic accident. Immediately after the crash he left his body and again found himself in a spiritual form invisibly hovering over the spot of the crash where he could see and recognise his mangled body. There was almost a humorous touch when he saw the ambulance-men collect his body to carry it to hospital. Without any special effort or intention he found himself following himself like a shadow right into the ambulance and then to the operating theatre in the hospital. It was then that he went back into his body to resume normal life.

This is not a rare phenomenon, and some meticulous

investigation is bound to bring many such occurrances to light. There are no religious principles involved but only plausible explanations which however may sound like scientific jargon to those who do not understand. This is what might have made many keep quiet about such experiences. They did not want others to think that they had gone mad, as they would have probably thought of others themselves in inversed circumstances.

Following the publication of one of my books which touched on such matters I was approached by a middle-aged man to solve what he described his difficult problem. Then he told me how on several occasions when lying down he found himself out of his body and floating in the air while all the time he was seeing his physical form lying on the bed in state of sleep. On the first occasion his reaction was that he was dead, until to his surprise he found himself back in his body as if nothing had happened. He had never spoken to anyone about it. Not even when it happened to him several times. He decided to talk to me after reading my book and learned that I could understand his plight. Of course, I did, and settled his problem. But hardly had I done that when he came up with another. This time he told me how he could not help getting to know what others were doing or saying while away from him. The man was undoubtedly a psychic, and this could be easily seen from his powerful eyes which tired anyone looking in them. Because of this he always wore sunglasses.

When such occurrances became public knowledge in Malta of the sixties they drew the awe and wonder that other innovations in local life were failing to raise. Astral projection was something which appealed to the imagination of people who came to know about it and were now thinking in terms of having been deprived of something that had been second nature to them. The relevant theory was being explained of how man had two bodies – the physical which is visible and an etheric one that is not. It has long been widely known, those interested were being told, that the etheric body could project itself out of the physical one and roam in suspension and in a spectral form. This was a statement that raised questions. Maybe there was even some scurrying about to read the right books which confirmed the new ideas that were being originated. But there was certainly no rush for the works of Dr Wiltse or H.G. Andrade, with their extraordinary feats attributable to astral projection like finding one's self in a free dimension and able to see London and New York on the instigation of a momentary thought. This question of roaming in a free dimension had often come up with reported cases of astral projection to foresee the future or even in reverse to see the past. What we know of the layout of Hookham Frere's house and garden of a hundred years ago was obtained in this way. It is claimed that Elizabeth, a daughter of the family which still tenant the house, had such an astral projection and could see as she can still describe the perfect layout, which for many years has been no more. This brings in the influence of Time, as exposed by Einstein. But such works would be too heavy and complicated for the conclusion that was being formulated in the Maltese mind with the usual simplicity. Then it came out. If a living human being could so easily be involved in an astral projection and roam as a spectre, then it followed that one need not have to be dead to become a ghost.

Heard just like that, this might have raised a laugh. But a case of such a ghost came to my attention. It concerned the family of my Maltese publisher. He had gone on a day's outing to the island of Gozo taking his wife and son Joseph with him. Two elder daughters had remained at home in Malta. At a time when it was known that parents and brother were in Gozo, one of the daughters was shocked to see her brother in a room she was cleaning. He was standing by a divan smiling at her, and wearing the clothes in which he had left that morning. Her first reaction was that she was only imagining things, but when the apparition persisted notwithstanding her attempts to dispel all thoughts of her brother she called her sister from another room. When she joined her, there was the sharp intake of breath as she also saw him. Until then there had been no thoughts of the occult, but now that both girls were seeing and confirming the same apparition they realised they were seeing a ghost, and both of them ran out of the room. In the evening when their brother returned with his parents from Gozo he was at a loss to know how he had projected himself.

What had by now become public knowledge about astral projection was by no means all. There was much more to come out, such as that the astral body which could so easily leave the physical one was an immortal spirit. And this generated two quick questions. If it was so easy for this etheric body to get out of its physical when this was still living, how much easier was it to leave it when dead? And when this is done, and there is no living physical body to return to, where would the immortal astral body go?

It began to look as if such assumptions had not only a bearing but were leading to a possible solution. There were no contradictions; no denials; nothing. Although unsaid there was a theory being made up that the immortal astral body could after all be the answer to ghosts. If one were to accept such supposition, then there could also be the answer to the question of energy to be manipulated by ghostly beings which was queried in the previous chapter, since many of those who have had out of the body experiences (astral projection) say that they invariably felt an electrical charge when their bodies separated. This could mean that the actual body is electrical in nature.

Presupposing that facts are as they are being assumed, could it not be possible for an astral body departed from its dead physical counterpart following an emotional death divert its electrical charge onto the surroundings to make it a prepared ground to generate the energy required for manifestations? This could be the answer for pattern and tragic/emotive ghosts.

Whether one accepts this suggestion or not, there is still bound to be a number of other questions remaining unanswered about inexplicable and yet exciting manifestations. There had certainly never been the intention and means to find such answers in Malta. Maltese involvement in the study of ghosts has been negligible. Whatever suggestions have ever been made were always in the way of simple and straightforward assumptions as have already ben described. Yet there had been occasions when the simple method of going by ocular evidence and common sense had paid dividends. In this case for energy to motivate psychic manifestations for example, the possibility of electrical energy forming part of the astral body could be a simpler description of the very common theory of energy activating ectoplasm which is said to play an important part in the materialization of ghosts.

Ectoplasm is a viscious substance forming the outer layer to protoplasm in the human body. It is said that it is susceptable to attraction by a bionic charge, and this is how it is alleged to be extracted from mediums to transfer to the ghost and make it function during seances. But by nature it belongs to the physical body, and after death most of it remains to decompose and finish with it. It is held however that some of it may be taken by the astral body when this separates and therefore becomes liable to polarisation by some force which until now seems to have not been properly identified. A theory that can be propounded could suggest this force as being the electrical charge contained in the astral body, which can thus be neutralized to become visible and take the shape of the person to whom it belonged. Hence the production of ghosts.

One point in support of this theory devolves from the tendency of any electrical charge to fluctuate in intensity and power for various reasons. It can even diminish through time and circumstances. Should such tendencies be also inherent in the charge under discussion, and if this exists, there would be such a likelihood, then this would strike a cogent note for hauntings by what is described as incongruous ghosts. Like for example the ball of mist. This was a very common type of haunting in Malta and there have been some interesting authentic manifestations which may after all wrap up this part of the occult and produce the much awaited solution.

Żabbar is a town of charm and contrast. It has its parts, old and new and these reflect the activity of the area. Towns are as much the same wherever. Żabbar however has the air of not belonging to the same kind of life now being reflected by the new urban areas being built up. It is still referred to as a village. But if it were ever justly considered as one it is no longer. Whatever changes have been made have still not changed the sense of timelessness – the feeling that the place had existed for ever, as if it had grown naturally out of the surrounding rural areas, some of which, alas, are no more.

There used to be until some years ago much fine countryside along the road which takes from this town to the city of Vittoriosa. A good wide road, passing beneath and astride Nicholas Cottoner Arch which still stands, surmounted by the bust of the Grandmaster whose name it bears. The legend says that the bust was placed in such a way that the figure's eyes are posed to look at a spot where a treasure in money and gold is hidden and still stands to be found. Once past the arch the road forks to the right past St Edward's College hidden behind a wall of cypress trees and oleanders in the right season, then swerving left on a short cut to the city. From this spot there is still a short walk before reaching the urban area along that part of the road which is full of long memories and a fruitful history. On the left there are fields neatly partitioned by ashlar walls, on the right tower the high bastions of Cottoner Curtain, standing blandly secure as they had been in the time of the Knights and still dwarfing the *Polverista*, a gunpowder store of those same times. The bastions and this building had seen the pageantry and bloodshed of the people who built them. Since then centuries rolled on with two great wars passing them by and leaving them untouched and unchanged but essentially medieval; and on them to-day sits lovingly the patina of time.

I have walked along that road many a time, but never in hours of darkness. There was others, similarily unimaginative, who wouldn't do it. Not because of any ghosts. There had never been any mentioned. But the place was ever so full of echoes of the past that it generated a feeling of mysterious awe which would someday, somehow, explode in some manifestaion.

Albert Farrugia was returning to Vittoriosa with a friend and his american wife. They had been to the festa at Żabbar, and being already past midnight chose this short cut to the city. Either that he was a sceptic or because of the companionship of his friends Albert had neither fears nor pre-occupations. Indeed, the bright moonlight and the cool September air made theirs a walk to be enjoyed. Far away a dog barked once and stopped. An owl snored in a high cypress of the cemetery that had been added to that spot. But for the rest there were only the undertones of night to accompany them.

Suddenly there was another sound. The clip clop of a donkey – and the squeaking wheels of the cart it was pulling.

Albert looked back and saw the flat cart with the driver sitting in front holding the reins. Tradition and circumstances made it obvious to him who that person could have been.

"It is Ausonio," he said to his companions. "He is returning from the festa."

"Who is Ausonio?" asked the american woman.

Then Albert told them about him. He was called *Sonu* for short. He earned his living making nougat, the local sweet delicacy that is traditionally sold at festas. He would take his wares and tables on his cart to the town or village en-fete, then return to Vittoriosa where he lived when celebrations are over. That man with the cart and donkey could not have been anyone else. Even his open shirt and waist-coat seemed to be familiar as he looked at him. There was also the cap which Ausonio always wore at an angle. As he still did until his recent demise.

All this, Albert's two companions could see as well, since the cart was by now quite close. There was a remark Albert made which for a second or two drew the others' attention. It wasn't more than that their eyes were off the man. When the three of them looked back there was nothing to be seen. Cart, man and donkey had disappeared into thin air.

There was another second or two of silence, as if all three were trying to find out whether they were imagining things. But indeed they were not. And the road lay wide and empty in the vague moonlight.

"What the hell is this?" asked the astonished woman.

"I don't know," replied her husband, similarly surprised.

Albert did not say anything. Because he couldn't

believe his eyes and he could not speak. But there was a shiver going through him as he realised that this could have been some supernatural phenomenon. And the three of them stood there in the moonlight, stunned into silence as if detached from all that was natural in life, and – alone. But were they alone?

There was suddenly something moving towards them. It was something small they had not noticed before. Now it was coming towards them from where the man and cart had last stood. It looked like a ball of knitting wool rolling on its way and gathering speed as if there was some power behind it. Horror seized the three of them as they leaped away to avoid being touched by the mysterious ball which went along between them. The could now see it better. It's texture was more like mist than wool, thick and uneven. It was more like white candy-floss, and there was a blast of cold air as it passed close by. They stood there, terrified and dumbfounded, following its progress as it moved away from them – fast and devilish towards Vittoriosa, until they could see it no longer.

It was then that the spell was broken, and Albert found his voice. "Oh, my God," he said, "I was never so frightened in my life. I know now how blind I had been." It was a simple statement which wiped out all the years he had been a sceptic. Now he knew that ghosts existed. No one would tell him any longer that they did not.

What however is of interest to our story is the deduction from this manifestation of another generality concerning ghostly apparitions. The manifestation by a ball of mist was nothing new in the history of ghosts in Malta. There had been several stories of similar manifestations. Indeed, some of the shrines and niches erected in deserted roads in bygone times had been intended to afford heavenly protection from such type of hauntings. The only variation had been in the description since the Maltese were always inclined to describe the ball as being made of wool. It was the nearest comparison they could make since mist was always very scarce and candy-floss was still unknown.

A case from the records of Ġużè Diacono concerns a haunting in Cospicua with such a manifestation which could qualify as being one where human beings had come the closest to this element of the world of ghosts. It happened in a house long known to be haunted by the traditional *hares*. There had been an occasion when a neighbour going into the house had seen a table full of silver money, but when she returned with members of the family who would not believe her found neither table nor money. It was only one of the tricks the *hares* was so often playing on them, exhausting their patience and endurance. When the married daughter of the family who lived in that same house could take it no longer she decided to leave there and then. She took up her baby and made to go out. Suddenly she was heard screaming in anguish. The rest of the family ran to her aid, and they could see that although unharmed she was badly frightened. She told them of the ball of mist which had suddenly appeared on the stairs as if to bar her way, and how on trying to go on she could not avoid stepping on it. The shock cost the woman her life.

Scepticism is often an instinctive reaction against an idea that seems abhorrent for no logical reason. But no one can blame those refuting cases of the ball of mist. They are cases which have proved to be difficult to understand even to those who believed in ghosts. Seen within the spectrum of experiences like the *Hares*, the returned spirits for suffrage, life pattern hauntings and tragic or emotive manifestations they looked senseless and incongruous. But one must face the fact that there is no doubt that they occurred. Moreover it was soon found out that mist, whether in the form of a ball or otherwise was also being encountered in hauntings in Britain. There too there had been no explanation.

In her book "Haunted East Anglia," Joan Forman mentioned at least eight occasions of mist believed to be part of a supernatural manifestation. But in one particular instance she mentions the case of one who was haunted in his lodgings by a ball of mist which rolled round the floor before moving up one of the walls until it came to the mantlepiece where is stationed itself and gradually took the form of a man's evil face. This and other similar cases with mist reported by other writers all came years after that which was happening in Malta and denying the locals a scope for comparison.

But even so, none of the writers seems to have been able to offer any explanation. It will have to be a Maltese effort to propound some theory which could suggest a basis of an explanation.

A significant factor which emerged in local cases was that on most of the occasions when a ball of mist materialised, there had been some other haunting by a different element. In the two cases mentioned for an example, there had in one case been the *hares* and in the other there was the man with cart and donkey. This leads one to believe in a connection between the two, as if it were a case of an apparition of the human form becoming a ball of mist or the other way round. There could therefore be some common factor and element in both apparitions and in others like them. Like the fluctuating power of energy behind the manifestation.

Ectoplasm is described and shown in infra-red photographs as being a substance which is white and cottony in appearance, but with its consistency being like that of mist, thinning or thickening according to some energy which could easily be the charge which makes it active. It may therefore not be beyond comprehension how such a charge can fluctuate in force, raising enough power to make a spirit take form of a fully fledged ghost or to be reduced and changed to a stage of active ectoplasm as the energy wears down. This could be the explanation behind the ball of mist. Such theory would conform to the occurrance mentioned as an example from the cases of Joan Forman with the ball of mist in her case becoming a human face and then reverting back to mist. There was even more conformity with my two Maltese examples wherein there were first the ghosts – the man with the cart and the *hares*, which in both cases reduced and turned themselves into active balls of mist.

It would also be logical to consider the possibility of diminished energy of ectoplasm. A case which might illustrate this concerned a friend of mine and his wife whose real names I have been asked to withhold. Before the events took place which I am going to relate, my friend was totally sceptical on the subject of the supernatural, and so was his fiancee (they had not yet married). This was not surprising since they were two down to earth persons all out to forge a good life together combining their varied interests in sports and healthy entertainment which by no stretch of imagination did it include ghosts. It was therefore to be expected that when faced with the common difficulty of their times of finding a house in town they took an old country house in a rural area bereft of modern facilities. There could be no consideration of their abode being further plagued with ghosts.

But when they got married and moved into the house, Anne (as I am calling her) was immediately struck by a sense of awe and mystery that at first she was describing as the air of the place in clinging desperately to its seclusion. It was indeed secluded, standing as it did like an island in time between two hamlets undetermined as to which diocese it belonged and unconnected to neither of the two in the most essential services like sewers and electricity. In fact the house was serviced by a cess pit, and for lighting resort had to be had to oil and pressure lamps.

It fell to these pressure lamps to bring a hint that all was not well in that place. When it was getting dark on their first day, and Alfred, the husband, had not yet returned home, Anne tried to light the lamps. She had done this before, but on that day every time she started a lamp going there was some sort of blowing which would come from nowhere to blow the flame out. Fortunately enough her husband arrived before she would have had to resign herself to a waiting vigil in darkness. In his hands the lamps worked at the first attempt.

The feeling of apprehension from that very first day they occupied that house was to remain with Anne for many days, and she tried to make the best of it by spending what time she could in the small garden or in the verandah outside as if wanting to avoid being alone inside. when because of the weather or the pressing kitchen chores she had to be inside then she would keep Hans close to her, the burly mastiff to which she somehow looked for protection. It was not the first time that having nothing to do she would lie down using the quietly curled dog as her pillow as if its warm strong body would succour her with patience and strength while waiting for her husband to return. Sometimes she would sleep and the hours of waiting would fly.

One day she was however awakened from her sleep by the dog moving beneath her. She thought he was only changing his position and lifted her head to let him free. But instead of lying down Hans slowly got upon his feet. Maybe he wanted to go out? But no. He stood still with his ears erect and his eyes looking steadily at the space that was between them and a wall, both empty of anything of attraction, and uttering a low growl. She told her husband about it when he returned and he would not think of some rational cause for the dog's action. But Anne was convinced the place was haunted. She found consolation in the fact that what ghost there could have been was not materialising.

There was however the day when it did. The waiting vigil had begun as usual with Anne sleeping and pillowing her head on the dog. This time Hans rose up quickly alive to something that was approaching which he could evidently sense. He tried to bark a challenge but finished by creeping back completely cowed. Anne was now afraid seeing the mastiff in that state, but her eyes and ears were alert for any sound or sight that she was feeling was bound to follow to herald what evil must have been approaching her. Then there was a wisp of mist or cloudy texture appearing in mid-ari out of nowhere which was soon getting bigger and materialising into a formless figure. There was at the same time a chill which seemed to pervade the very marrow of her bones, and which was distinctly sharper than the cold of fear that was all over her. It must be said that the dog did not abandon her and stood by her legs. But she could feel him shaking in his skin. Then when she could bear it no more she ran away from the room.

When Alfred returned he could see the change in Anne. He believed what she told him, but what could he do? They had a priest to bless the place in the way of exorcism, and the poor soul would go about the place sprinkling holy water and reciting prayers obviously terrified. There were four other occasions when there was the same manifestation. On two occasions there was Alfred with her, but he would not see anything. Not even when he would go towards where Anne would point to him, and walk right through the apparition without feeling anything. The climax came when with the fifth occasion as the apparition approached Anne there was the form of a hand – a five fingered badly mangled over sized hand which came out of the undefined ghostly figure, as if to touch her as she was walking backwards away.

Luckily they managed to find a house in town to where they moved. It was then that friends and relatives told them that they knew all the time that the country house had been haunted. They had not told them before not to alarm them since they had nowhere to go. The landlord must have known too since he himself asked them whether they were leaving after having seen some ghost.

This haunting had made such an impression on Alfred that even in his peaceful new home in town he would not rest until he could get to the bottom of it all. Reviewing the manifestations step by step he concluded that it must have been a ghost which for some reason or other could not materialise completely. Enlightened by bits of information he got from here and there he was not far wrong in concluding there had been not enough energy to generate the ectoplasm in the making of a spectre.

The ghost? It was said to be that of a young woman who had lived in that house during the French occupation (1798/1800), and whose cousin had worked for the occupying forces against the interests of the Maltese until his traitorous deeds were discovered. Believing that his female cousin had betrayed him to the Maltese he had hanged her in that room which her spectre must have haunted throughout the years diminishing by time to the incomplete manifestation that troubled Anne and Alfred.

But even here Maltese beliefs would not rest on theories however reasonable they may appear to be. There had to be some indication or confirmation of the truth. Not through some scientific treatise or mathematical theorem but through something simpler and clearer which could be easily understood by all. It seems that even here one of the ghosts of Malta obliged with a spectacular haunting just when it was most needed –

in the late sixties.

Manwel Dimech Street which at the time of the manifestation was called Prince of Wales Road is one of the busiest streets in Sliema. Shops, boutiques and department stores line its sides. There is hardly an hour of the day when there isn't a crowd, and walking in it during shopping hours becomes a nightmare. It was at such a time that my first hand witness whom I am calling Pawla Cassar was going along this street when she happened to raise her eyes as her attention was drawn by the sound of a window opening on the second floor of a house. To her shocking surprise she saw a woman climbing on the window sill, stand there for a moment and then with open arms hurtle herself forward for a suicidal fall. For one moment Pawla saw the woman falling down, and she screamed. Then before her eyes the falling body disappeared and dropping to the ground in its place there was a ball of mist which fell on the pavement only a few feet away from her.

Her scream had drawn many eyes to the open window, but all that could then be seen was the dropping white ball which looked like one of wool that might have been dropped inadvertedly and certainly not justifying Pawla's alarm.

But her scream had also brought out a female from her shop which was in the ground floor just beneath the window on which all eyes seemed to be still fixed. The shopkeeper looked at the ball of mist still on the pavement in front of her shop, and to the surprise of all those who were near was heard grumbling and saying as if to the ball: "Why did you have to do it at this time?"

From investigations carried out it resulted that there had indeed been a woman who had killed herself by falling from that window many years before. This left no doubt that the manifestation was a replay of that violent and emotional moment. It appeared however that for some reason like a flash reaction at the moment of falling the woman could have reduced the resultant energy which changed the manifestation from that of the spectral form of her bodiless spirit to one of a ball of mist retaining the pattern throughout the following years of haunting. That it always happened so was evidenced by the shopkeeper's remarks.

Apart from its fantastic effect this haunting might have provided the long awaited definition of the ball of mist. More than this there might also have been an explanation and pointer at the possible reaction of energy on ectoplasm and the generation of ghosts.

Chapter 9

Progress and Poltergeists

If I had to pick on a period of time when the ghosts of Malta had to withstand their biggest test I would undoubtedly go for the seventies. Those were years of change and upheaval for the island now to be divested of all remaining foreign military installations. This would mean the end of British military presence in Malta. There would obviously also be the end of the Maltese connection with NATO. Whatever was the opinion of the average Maltese, NATO was sent away. Yet its member countries and Britain agreed to pay for the British stay and began to fork out between them a rental of fourteen million pounds a year for seven years, plus a part grant part soft loan of two and a half million pounds in economic aid from Italy apart from technical help from other countries. This agreement would sustain the island until 31st March 1979, when all foreign forces would have to leave and their facilities be withdrawn.

This signified a new era with Malta taking her own decisions which for better or for worse were being laid down and accepted by all those concerned. The island's long standing status was to be changed to one of a democratic republic with a Maltese President. But until then there was to be the first ever Maltese Governor-General. This was after five Civil Commissioners and thirty four Governors, all British, since 1799. This first significant honour was bestowed on Sir Anthony Mamo who was then Chief Justice. With the establishment of a republic as their ultimate aim the Maltese people were geared up in the way of new beliefs and levels to be reached. If one could talk so confidently about a country's emancipation it was to be expected that the same would be done with every factor that was involved in life. Everyone was suddenly being given the push and obligation to think big and pull his weight in the new pattern of life that was being set where there was a place for everything. Except for ghosts.

This explains why for many the idea of ghosts had suddenly become an anathema. With the background of a new materialistic kind of life the average Maltese was now finding it incredible of anyone coming back from death in any way or form. This had now become a common philosophy, and to substantiate it there was again the same old explanation in the way of a new party-line that ghosts were no longer in evidence.

Such a sweeping statement might have then been justified since with post-war reconstruction completed, the new government had launched a drive to demolish remaining slums. It was therefore to be expected that many haunted premises would give up their ghosts.

Even so, there were new elements qualifying for the occult which now began coming to light. People were reading and learning more, obviously becoming more willing, indeed anxious, to be enlightened with new ideas. The subject of Reincarnation was one of them. It was something that had been heard of before but it was now that it was widely popularized by several writers all over the world. Still, however fascinating it was, there had as yet not been offered any hard evidence for this phenomenon. As indeed there hasn't been until to-day. It could be understood that the main cause behind proving reincarnation was to provide proof of survival after death. But such proof had always existed with the Maltese in their religion. There had also been ample proof of such survival in their ghosts, which had now become so scarce.

This might have failed to produce the expected enthusiasm that was then being reflected in other countries, but the biggest objection to the theory of reincarnation in Malta obviously came from the church. This was understandable since such a theory was blatantly going against its teachings on man's destiny in everlasting life after death. Any Maltese would be willing to discuss reincarnation. Maybe even offering sensible suggestions, but deep in every heart there would always be reasonable comparisons and allowances to be made. If after death man is destined to be rewarded or punished for his deeds during his life on earth how can he be expected to reincarnate? One of these two theories must be wrong. With Maltese reasoning already substantiated by various proofs of the former theory, even with the help of ghosts, it became immediately obvious that the latter theory must have been the wrong one.

Anyone believing in reincarnation might have raised the same question in regard to the belief in man's last appointment with God to finish in heaven or hell. But here there were no problems. Spirits returning for suffrage did so on the strength of special grace allowed to them. Most of the rest were cases of tragic and emotional imposition. Where they were not, the Maltese clamped down and threw the weight of their reply on their faith which had already some mysterious dogmas to be believed without question, even if they were not understood.

Even with the people having now become more broad-minded and open to all kinds of theories and beliefs there was always the religious element at the bottom of every innermost feeling and resulting conclusion that was always bound to win the day. This had been Maltese life for twenty centuries, and there had as yet appeared nothing forceful enough to change it. There was a time when Maltese crossed themselves before embarking on a bus trip or went into the water for a swim. This was now rarely being done. There had also been the kissing of bread before eating it (symbolising the taking of Holy Eucharist), the crossing with the thumb of the mouth when yawning (to keep the devil from entering it), the prayers that were said at every conceivable moment of the day. All this is done no more by average person, the usage no doubt losing importance in the materialistic times. The Maltese are of course no angels, as indeed they never were. They swear, slander, steal and swindle; they also fornicate and murder. But they would never miss Sunday Mass; in the same way that they would not let the opportunity of doing a good deed go by undone. All the wrong and evil done, however, they would one day confess and repent from, and whatever happens they will finally return to the fold of their faith. That is why they would never subscribe capriciously to any principle that goes against it. This is why the theory of reincarnation had never made a footing amongst them. In their good old characteristic way they would listen to everything, read what is given to them, and even discuss when necessary. But they will only believe what they want to believe.

It had become the same case with ghosts in general. Their existence, where it was believed, was neatly classified in some form of order. The returned dead asking for suffrage (which not even the sceptic would refute), the pattern, tragic and emotive hauntings which had been wrapped up in a possible solution, and the incongruous or senseless manifestations which were now being seen in a better light. There was only one other type of ghost remaining outstanding and not yet accounted for. The restless spirit which made the inexplicable poltergeist.

It had already been evidenced that through its haunted years Malta had had more than its share of poltergeistic activity. This local ghost could certainly not qualify to be a spirit returning for suffrage. Nor could it be considered in a life pattern haunting, or as one belonging to tragic or emotive circumstances. The difference in its manifestations confirmed this. There had been various definitions of the poltergeist all over the world, but a very likely one was that given by Allan Kardec of an undeveloped spirit playing naughty games and occasionally becoming really violent. This seems to have been reflected in a school of thought maintaining that a poltergeist, with the word deriving from the German *poltern* (to make noise) and geist (ghost) does not hurt humans it haunts. Indeed, the implication is that it is a ghost that haunts by noise, although it is an undenied fact that the poltergeist haunts also by ocular occurrence. In whatever way it haunts, I would add, it can certainly drive people out of their wits.

If we were to line out the various poltergeistic manifestations that have occurred in Malta throughout time, and particularly during the last forty years when such occurrences were identified for what they were, the list would read like a catalogue of every trick these ghosts were able to play. All types of noises, raps, footsteps – walking and climbing stairs, dragging chains, billowing sails, bangs and crashes. There had also been furniture thrown about, levitation, stoning and displacement of babies and objects from one place to another. All this besides the harmless teasing by water taps which seems to be a favourite prank with poltergeists.

The truth of this can be evidenced by the hundreds of cases on record, some of which have already been mentioned elsewhere. A respectable list whch is incomplete since now that haunted houses had become scarce, yet more cases of poltergeistic activity are still coming to light. Like the case related to me by a reliable priest who remembers the occasion when he was still a child and the *hares* (it was still considered as one there being no differentiation between a poltergeist and a ghost) flinging him from the roof of his house into a courtyard in front of his terrified mother, without being burt. Lawrence, another person I interviewed, told me of the nasty prank played on him when one day while on his way home, he saw tongues of flame and smoke emitting from the roof of his house. Even though he had had an intimation that his house could prove to be haunted because of the spot it stood on where sixteen people had been killed in an air-raid shelter during the war, he did not attribute the fire to any ghostly manifestation. This was of course for the simple reason that he had never sensed, heard or seen any ghosts. Indeed he was now struck by the strange fact that although there were people in the street going about their business none of them was sparing as much as a glance at the blazing building. Still, he ran the last few yards home to find his wife and children undisturbed, and the only fire to be seen was the one in the cooker.

There was also the nerve wrecking case of a capuchin monk who would often have spells of having to watch pictures being taken off the wall in his cell as if handled by unseen hands and to find them back on the floor after he would have restored them to their place. The nuns of a well-known convent in the sister-island of Gozo had to leave the convent en-bloc one fateful night, terrified and literally driven away by the antics of a poltergeist. The case was hushed down, as if rather than divulging details they would prefer to believe that such ghosts were of the devil, and therefore not to be admitted within the realms of possibility. But there was a whole streetful of neighbours to witness the strange exodus of the clamouring nuns.

It will be noticed that in all these cases like many others the poltergeist seemed more inclined to harass than to hurt. This is characteristic of most of Malta's poltergeists. They are slick and fastidious, with an uncanny sense of timing that could almost indicate some sort of intelligence behind the ghostly activities. This is why they can outsmart anyone brave enought to take them on. There have then been the malevolent ones some of which have also been mentioned. They could be evil in their intentions as belong to mortal beings. The saintly priest Dun Ġorġ Preca who has been mentioned in connection with miracles had until his death kept a stone on his desk which a malevolent poltergeist had thrown at him when he entered a haunted room in one of the religious doctrine centres the priest had founded. Fortunately enough, poltergeists were always attached to a particular spot or house rather than a person; so anyone could get rid of their mischievous attentions by simply changing residence. The other remedy was exorcism, which proved the spirit involved to have been more than a straightforward poltergeist.

This question of changing house because of ghosts gave people ideas.

It was now 1975. The new Constitution of Malta had been enacted, and on 13th December 1974 the island had officially become a democratic republic. The monarchial system of Government had been abolished and the post of Governor General was replaced by one of a President which was filled by Sir Anthony Mamo. There were still four more years, and one more election to go for the day when Malta would remove the British base which government had already labelled as a date with destiny. But if there were indeed such a destiny its outcome would not be left to chance. The Maltese had to make it. The clarion call was given. Everyone was expected to work towards such aim. To a now more benevolent Libya, keenly interested in having Malta dispose of all foreign bases which could pose a threat there were discreet suggestions made to define the Median Line which would allow the island a part of the sea bed between the two countries where to dig for oil. But this was going to be a long process while it had now become the time for quick results. These could only be obtained on the home front.

To the thousands who had been drafted into a Pioneer Corps from the dole lists there was now added a few more thousands in a similar corps pecurialy called *Dirgħajn il-Maltin* (Maltese Arms). If the unemployed had to get paid they might as well work for what they were getting. The island had become like a colony of ants with the leaders calling for work and more work of which they wanted to see the product. Whether or not there was the expected result their shouting became a slogan to be lived with night and day allowing nothing else to be voiced which would detract anyone from the given purpose. It had suddenly become like blaspheming to admit belief in ghosts. This would certainly not help in the work revolution that had been launched, and to bring in something that did not reflect endeavour and effort could be tantamount to madness.

A very significant factor emerged here when the demand for newly built houses by government was much bigger than the supply. There were many who had to make a strong case for an imperative change in residence to the allocating authority. Cases were various. Illness, lack of space, unhygienic conditions and increasing families. But even in that year of the Lord 1975 when man was waiving aside all mention of ghosts as taboo, there were the applicants for new houses submitting as a case the fact that their residence was haunted.

Was this true to fact? Or was it a case of people

getting ideas? Whatever it was many of them were strangely enough asking their doctors to certify the evidence. They would first call them to deal with a case of nerves or fear; then a story of the haunting would be told. Whether cases were genuine or a hoax, doctors were not being taken for a ride. The applicants could not have picked on worse sponsors with most doctors being sceptics.

Maybe even they were wrong, and taking too much for granted.

There was one of them I tackled about the matter. He was a young popular upcoming physician whose name I do not intend to mention. Neither do I want to indicate the town where he had his practice. It will suffice to say that it was one fecund with stories of ghostly manifestations until many of its buildings were swamped beneath the waves of reconstruction. The doctor was a sceptic and he made no bones about it. He might even have been a little cynical when telling me that he was surprised how a writer like me should believe in such things. He attributed ghostly manifestations to hallucinations and impressions. That was all there was to it, he said. Then he went on to give me an example by telling me of something that had just happened to him.

It seemed that he had been called to make a nightly call on a patient who lived in a deserted outskirt of the town which was not yet developed. It was in a wilderness of rocks, ferns, trees and brambles. He had to leave his car some distance away and walk the rest of the way to his patient's house. There was not a sound other than his footsteps as he walked. "Not a rustle of a gravecloth" he said with a sardonic smile.

"But," he told me, "I could see in the distance the oil lamp over the gate of a cemetery and the packed shadows of the tall cypress trees."

"It appears that the sight affected you," I said.

"Not in the way you put it," he replied. "But there was my father buried in that place, and I could not help remember him."

Then he continued to say how he kept thinking about his father as he climbed a flight of stairs to his patient's first floor flat. But suddenly he paused in his speech as if thinking about something he had left out. Then to my surprise he said: "I want to be honest and say that whilst going up those stairs I did have a strange feeling."

"What kind of feeling?" I asked.

"I cannot describe it," he said, "but it was as if ... there was some other presence with me on those stairs."

"Well ..." I began saying. And I could not help laughing at the stance he had suddenly taken.

"No," he said cutting my words short. "It wasn't what you think. I knew that what I was feeling was brought about through my thinking so deeply about my father. My proximity to his place of rest at that time of the night must have made a too strong impression upon me."

So he continued to say how after he left his patient he was again engulfed in thoughts about his father. Then when half way down the stairs he suddenly felt something or somebody pushing him from behind, and before he knew it went tumbling down the rest of the stairs. I was tempted to say "There you are." But I anticipated what he would be saying.

"That was something," he said, "that anyone might have attributed to a ghost – the *hares*, as it is called. But let me tell you it was nothing of the sort. It was just my imagination that caused it all. I might even after all have slipped on those steps."

There was a lot I wished to say to him, but I knew it was no use going into explanations with sceptics like him. So I simply told him to be careful should he happen to go there again. And I made sure to sound cynical.

As I came to know later what I did not say to him was said by his wife when he returned home. She must have believed in ghosts.

The story might have ended there without any conclusion had I not met the doctor again a few months later. This time he looked so happy to meet me.

"Ah, there you are," he said. "I have been trying so much to see you lately."

"Why? What's happened?" I asked.

For a moment he looked at me without saying anything as if thinking on his next words. Then he blurted out: "It's about that place I was talking to you about when we were last together."

"Are you referring to the place where you slipped down the stairs?" I asked again.

"Yes."

"Well? What about it?"

"I was called there again," he said, this time I noticed the cynical note was missing.

"Yes?" I said, encouraging him to go on.

"My wife had believed that on that first occasion it must have been a ghost which had pushed me down those stairs. This time when I was going on my second call she reminded me of that first occasion, and I took the hint. I remembered your warning too, even if it had been a cynical one. This second time I wanted so much to prove you and my wife wrong, and I was so careful."

"And what happened?" I asked.

"First of all I took it upon myself to avoid thinking about the cemetery and my father. But I still had that same feeling that I was not alone as I was going up those stairs. The place seemed to feel more eerie which, I must confess, I attributed to auto-suggestion brought about by my awareness of what I had to prove to you and to my wife."

"Well?" I asked.

"The feeling was stronger when I was on my way out. This time I held on to the bannisters as I went down, and took the stairs carefully, one by one."

"All right," I said, "and nothing happened. So you proved your point . . ."

"No," he interrupted my flow of words, "hold it. It wasn't like that."

"Then what?" I asked when I saw him pause.

"Half-way down the stairs, there was that push again, and even with my preparedness, I was sent tumbling down those stairs again."

I didn't say anything, and for the first time began to notice a couple of bruises in his face which were healed, and which I had certainly not noticed on the previous occasion we had met. I found I was almost happy for the way things had turned out, and I was ashamed for harbouring such a thought. But the doctor did not seem to notice what was passing through my mind.

"You were right, of course," he said, "I don't know

how, but ghosts must exist. It was certainly one of them which had twice sent me tumbling down those stairs. It must have been a poltergeist that did it. Isn't that what you call them?"

"Yes," I said. "It must have been a malevolent one."

The astonishing element was that this poltergeist had to strike at a time when talk and thoughts about ghosts had dissipated and belief in them was no more. Not even as an interlude to alienate and divert attention from some rigid element of existence in the way of progress. To drive this in there had to be another poltergeist.

There was one that was still roving in San Anton Palace, now housing a Maltese President. The inhabitants might have known of the moor that had haunted the place since the governorship of Lord Methuen (1915 – 1919). Besides other manifestations there had been the detaining of the Bishop of London in his room. It could be therefore that they might have associated the restless steps and noises they heard so often in one particular room to this. With the palace being the residence of a head of state it will not be surprising if the incidence of such manifestations was hushed. But when the silence in the palace began to be broken by the devilish banging of a door, all the servants heard it and knew what it implied. They would talk. Even if they didn't, there was the night when, I was told, the inhabitants of the palace were so terrified that they had to leave the place in whatever clothes they had on. The door that was opening and shutting itself to cause the infernal noise was the same one that had similarily bothered the English bishop sixty years before. His exorcism must have worn off, and the haunting moor was at his old tricks again.

But this time it was not to be something so restricted that was wanted; to be discussed in low tones behind the walls of high society. But one to come into the open and toe the day's line of free publicity by making headlines.

John, as I am calling the head of the family destined for the debacle, had always been attracted to the town of Birkirkara. He was born there when it was still a suburb and had to be away from it only because of circumstances beyond his control. But when he came to change his place of business it might have been more by conscious design than fate that he found the shop he wanted in his old town. It was now no longer old. The years had given it wide and long streets, newly built white stoned housing estates and a few more thousands of inhabitants which made of it a good business proposition. Even in a compressed small island like Malta, so few miles made a distance, and so short a distance made a difference. Maybe it was this, coupled no doubt with his old love for the town that made him try and find also a residence there.

It turned out that he was not destined to wait long for within a few months there was just the place he wanted. A maisonette in a newly developed street where John soon had his family settled, for the kind of life they had all yearned for.

There were months of a peaceful life to follow. Each and every member of the family was blessing the decision that had been taken, when suddenly there was something strange happening to John.

It happened one day when he was alone in the house, and there was the sound of something metallic dropping to the floor in the next room. John went to see what had caused the sound and to his surprise found a metal ashtray on the floor where it had obviously dropped.

A simple enough explanation. But the last time he had seen that ashtray, which was only half an hour before it had been on the piano. There were no cats or dogs in the house; he was alone. All windows were closed, and even if there had been any wind blowing on that day, which there wasn't, it could not have blown that ashtray to the floor. Then who or what had made it drop?

Much as he searched his mind, he could not find a possible answer. So he just let it go at that, and placed the ashtray back in its place. Hardly had he gone into the other room when again he heard the ashtray falling to the floor. This time he quickly looked into the room and saw the ashtray was again on the floor where it had obviously been dropped by some agency which he could not see. Getting suddenly rattled he did not pick it up, but just ran out of the house, not knowing what to do or where to go.

The next hour or two must have been the worst he had ever experienced in life. He walked aimlessly along the streets turning the fantastic occurrance in his mind but without getting anywhere in the way of a conclusion. Except of course that his house was haunted.

He had decided not to say anything to his wife and children not to alarm them. Fortunately enough for the next couple of days there were no other manifestations. But John was now a terrified man, and his wife had noticed how he had suddenly preferred to go out when there was nobody else at home. In the tried security of their personal relations she had been driven to conclude that there was something bothering him. She could see it in his actions as well as in the look of perplexity that she was often catching in his eyes. She tried to get it out of him. But all the sweet words and caresses she produced could not do it. Was he ill? Or was there something wrong with his business? No, nothing of this. Then what could it be?

But the uneventful days seemed to have lulled John into a false feeling of security. "Maybe it had all been my imagination after all" he mused. then he began to show a normal appearance even if it was only for the benefit of his family.

The wife was still not deceived and pressed him for his reasons, until he was costrained to tell her. She tried to laugh his worries off. And she might have succeeded had not the poltergeist struck again.

This time there was the whole family at home when there was a crashing sound in the next room. They all ran to see what it was, and stood dumbfounded on seeing what had once been a beautiful porcelain vase on a centre table was now smashed to smithereens on the floor.

The wife knew immediately how John had been right. Her first instinctive move was to make the sign of the cross. As she did, hell seemed to be let loose in that room. First the chandelier began swaying as if there was some weight forcing it to move. Then chairs, tables and even the piano began to be levitated in the air as if to be thrown about. At this moment all of them ran out of the house. But not before a heavy iron bolt came whizzing through the air missing John by a fraction of an inch.

That night they didn't return home and went to stay with relatives. But their hurried get away was noticed by neighbours and before they knew it the poltergeist at Birkirkara became news. It was an occasion for debate which in contrast with the extreme importance of political and development upheavals then raging in the country left no doubt to the heartiness of the people's appetite for ghosts and their stories. For a few days there was suddenly less importance being given to international affairs. There was even dampened the fervour for the general election which would decide amongst other things whether British services would have to leave Malta for ever. Indeed it was a hectic time with more important news than ghosts qualifying for the headlines, but even the newsmen who are by virtue of their profession sceptical of anything they can't see and interview, seemed to be inclined to play to their readers' whims by devoting columns to the unusual Birkirkara incident.

While all this was going on, John was at his wits' ends for what to do. He had no other place to go to and could not just leave his house to the devil that must have inhabited it. He expressed himself in such terms through the agitation he was in, but it must have been a devil that had invaded the sanctity of his house, he was told, in the form of a damned spirit. The only remedy lay in exorcism. This time even the Church was of the same opinion and a priest was detailed to exorcise.

It might have been his first experience of the kind. Even if it weren't, Maltese priests do not cherish such duty, although they do it. Armed only with his prayer book, a cross and holy water, the priest entered the house, and in a loud voice as if to give him much needed courage, began to invoke God's assistance for his debacle. Hardly had he mentioned the name of God when things began to lift themselves from shelves and began flying in his direction. He took up the holy water to sprinkle about him. It was at that moment that a two inch iron nut which had appeared from nowhere flew at his head. But it encountered the water from his sprinkler a foot away from his forehead, and to his amazement it stopped in its trajectory and dropped harmlessly at his feet. It was as if the holy water had taken away all the diabolical force that was behind it.

The house became suddenly silent as the priest continued with his assignment. Only his footsteps could be heard in the rooms that had been the scene of that diabolical haunting. And his voice reciting the beautiful words of the exorcism of St Michael. That was that. John was given back his house, and the newspapers their last news. The people went back to their politics and election, as if the episode had only been a brief interlude to detract the tension that had gripped the country in anticipation of that which had more meaning to them than ethereal ghosts.

Chapter 10
Towards a Climax

In 1976 the election was over, and the current government was booked for a further five years of office. Considering the important decisions that were to be taken during this period the event could be said to be of much significance. There were the expected human failings in evidence with some crying for joy, others for sorrow. But none cried for ghosts. It appeared that they had gone once and for all out of circulation. It would of course have been the same story had there been a different result to the election. The ostracization of ghosts had become a part and parcel of the new times. But were the ghosts of Malta destined to have such an ignominious end after all?

In truth it could be said that the case for ghosts had not been packed and completely thrown away by all. So much so that only a few months after the election, and this was in 1977, a band of enthusiasts formed a local Parapsychology Society with the obvious intention of cultivating knowledge about this fantastic subject and also to expand it through further research. That there was still a following I can vouch myself since I was very much impressed with the interested audience that attended a talk I had occasion to deliver to this society. But at the time that this body came into being there were other societies being formed in aid of other activities more intrinsically connected with the new times of life that would not wait. This element of hurry had now become a local characteristic. Strike while the iron is hot. Get a decision at the first time of asking; tomorrow may be too late. If there were a law and reason both had to prevail in anything one was being expected to do. Never before had there been such a show that none could any longer be expected to be trusted aside or led by the nose.

That there were still differing opinions to every question could be seen from the correspondence columns in the press, mostly from rival political factions which were very often finishing in court for libel. Indeed, either because of the new situation or of an attitude wherein people could no longer care to be bothered to argue, every trivial disagreement was being taken to court to the extent of handicapping work with the enormous volume of suits that were being lodged. It was no doubt a healthy sign of the democratic element, but oe could not help concluding that there was much loss of time and effort with every conceivable matter that was inconsistent or of a controversial nature. Maybe it was the right occasion to have ghosts submitted to a judicial body before being ignored. But there wasn't as far as I know any law suit about them since many years back when the subject had been hotter and more challenging. This was either because any two parties involved – those who believed and the others who did not – had established their stand and would not look for a third opinion, or simply because what could be established had already been done in that previous occasion mentioned. Indeed on that occasion a very important judgement on the existence of ghosts had been given by Judge Montanaro-Gauci which had made headlines in its days and had until now been remembered. Had the courts admitted the existence of ghosts?

The case in question had been instituted by a person who had bought an empty house and then learned that it was haunted. So he sued the seller to release him from the contract of purchase alleging that he had sold it to him when knowing it was not habitable because of ghostly manifestations that occurred in it. If the purchaser had his good reasons to lodge his suit because of what he believed in that the house was haunted, so was the seller justified in defending the suit because of the defamatòry allegations that were made on the house which could easily stick in a small place like Malta.

The evidence submitted by the appellant to substantiate his allegation came from the wife of the last tenant of that house. She said that whilst living there she had often heard sounds of human groaning coming from the well. There had been no possibility of anyone else having groaned to be mistaken for a paranormal occurrance since this happened when she was alone in the house. There had also been occasions when she heard the lid to the well open and shut by itself. When she could stick it no longer she ran away from the house and went to stay with a neighbour. This neighbour was also called to give evidence, saying that she knew of an earlier tenant who had experienced the same manifestations. There was also a third neighbour to say that when on one occasion she had called on a tenant of the allegedly haunted house the door was opened by a man wearing a blue cassock. She had run away terrified then, knowing that her neighbour's husband was abroad, and assuming that the man she saw must have been a ghost. Indeed, the tenant herself had left the house later on learning that it was haunted.

The defendant did not try to disprove the existence of ghosts. All he did was to produce a number of witnesses who at some time or other had lived in that house without hearing or seeing any manifestations. There was also one witness who admitted having heard noises on occasions, but always finding later a rational explanation.

The important factor for the argument on ghosts did not lie as much on the outcome of the suit as on the decision of the court on whether it would admit action on a case of ghosts. The judge did not only confirm that such action was admissable but also quoted local and foreign jurisprudence at length on which he based his decision. The fact that the appellant lost the case as his witnesses could not rule out alternative rational causes for the manifestations had no bearing on the matter in discussion. The ghosts had on that occasion won the day. A contrast to the current time when they were at their lowest ebb.

It was to be noticed however that there were more things other than ghosts that had faded out of the new life as having been given the cold shoulder by those making themselves the pioneers riding the waves of progress and modernism. And many of these discarded things were now coming back after having proved their values in the characteristic of a nation even during their term of exile. No matter, for example, how many of the old Maltese culinary arts had been superceded by new systems and types of cooking brought over by the many imported chefs to teach the locals, Maltese recipes were coming back after being temporarily buried. Big and modern hotels which had gone up like mushrooms with their sophisticated cuisine and restaurants were again serving stewed Maltese rabbit, delicious *timpana* and other traditional dishes which never lacked patronage by the 339,537 tourists that had been clocked during 1976. Mentioning mushrooms, there had also been a quick and unexpected return to the old catacombs and air-raid tunnel shelters of the war which gave better scope for their cultivation than the methods imported by foreigners. The Maltese wholesome crusty bread had in the meantime resisted the onslaught of the foreign type baked in the latest automatic ovens, and Maltese bakers stuck to their own primitive stone contraptions to the delight of locals and foreigners alike.

In the industrial sector too, the local worker was making a name for himself through ingenuity and dexterity which had returned or in certain cases had never departed from the methods and tools inherited from his forefathers. In some cases these even bettered the modern and more streamlined ways that were introduced. A British firm perturbed by many of its refrigerators being returned because of a common fault which they could not repair did not believe that a local was remedying such fault on his own in Malta. When it sent its engineers to see for themselves they were amazed to learn that what their sophisticated methods failed to do, was being done by a self-taught native technician with the most primitive of tools and at a fraction of the cost. The imported idea of building in concrete for example, had for some years almost ousted the local way for quick erection of buildings. Now it was being realised it was no match for the old locally quarried stone. The only accepted compromise was to retain the introduced cutting machinery in the quarries in preference to manual methods. For the rest, however, the heavy Malta stone would still be lifted by hands, carried on the shoulder and laid in place on a cushion of mortarised dust and water. This had been the method of the Knights, and was to remain for ever.

This was a movement that was being advertised as holding Maltese traditional arts and culture. But it was more in the way of sticking to what had been genuine and authentic which would not submit to any artificial wave of modernism.

Could it not be the same case with ghosts? They were far from being just a Maltese tradition. Ironically enough as they were being forcefully ousted out in Malta, the elements that had composed them were being proved and clarified elsewhere. There had been the wonderful continued research by Dr Raymond Moody of America which had culminated in the two already mentioned books he had written bringing about more reflections on astral projection and the immortality of the spirit. To boost the theory of existing electrical energy in the astral body with its effect to materialise and motivate ghosts there had always been the simple scientific principle of the electric charge in motion setting up a magnetic field. But now there was the astounding news of the alleged fantastic Philadelphia Experiment to show how magnetism could indeed by the transposition of molecules shoot solid objects and human beings into other dimensions and making them disappear to be transported to different locations with the ease and speed attributed only to astral projection. It must of course be said that the United States Department of the Navy to whom this experiment was attributed has always denied that it had ever taken place. But whether or not this was so, it cannot be denied that the *Field Theory* on which it was based was found and uncovered by Einstein and it exists. From what is known this theory could produce the answer to the mysterious disappearances in the Bermuda Triangle. Why should it not therefore produce a new theory on ghosts?

There were now more things, systems and usages which were still coming back. Whether it was because of local origin or due to the changing world situation with its evident resort to artificiality which was no match for the genuine, there was a wind of change blowing. A more sober return to the aristocratic villa type of building or the characteristic local style of terrace house was evident. This was in place of the square featureless and impersonal blocks that had wormed their way in Maltese post-war architecture. With the many new industries that had been imported and adopted there were again flourishing the old local callings in pottery work and lace-making. Old techniques with Malta stone and glass were revived. The casino kept attracting more clients, but the good old government weekly lotto retained its attraction to a bigger nuber of stakers.

I must interrupt myself to make it plain that I am not trying to say that the country was reverting to its old pre-war life. Far from it. It was only a case of bringing back or retaining the old which was genuine with the new. While theatregoers could now have English and Italian plays by foreign companies or their Maltese adaption by locals, there were those who still languished after the old type of farce which began coming back. People began to dine out and enjoy floor-shows, but they still had their *festas* with bands and fireworks. It had indeed become a more colourful life. Maybe even more cosmopolitan. No wonder that the end of 1978 had for that year clocked a bigger number of tourists – 477,741.

It may appear that I should not have encroached so much on ground which belongs to history when my concern is with ghosts. It seemed to me however that without at least some account of the singular efforts that were being made in refinding the genuine of past times I could not give plausibility to the fact that ghosts were not being included in such a revival. In Malta as anywhere else ghosts had been old as time. They were still being talked about. But the grave way of expression when talking about them had now turned into gay. The reflective had become playful. For the rest there was silence. The church never pronounced itself. Not even on the kind of ghosts that pertained to an element of her teachings. A government which had never bothered about ghosts and their curriculum in history was not to be expected to start now when it was dead intent on the most important part of its programme which was to have the departure for ever of British forces from Malta. This was also a weight on one's mind.

It is true to say that the Maltese had always believed in their characteristic ability to surmount difficulties and emerge victorious in whatever turmoil they might find themselves in. Their chequered history confirms this. But it was no mean feat to sever a connection after 180 years. What if it was all wrong? What if all the substitutes being suggested were all to be make-believe? This had become a pre-occupation. The thousands of employees with the services who were already being diverted to other jobs as the garrison was being run down created an additional problem for those having to adapt themselves to a new life afresh. They would take the longest to forget. It was to be expected that there would be a certain amount of trepidation which would certainly leave no mind for ghosts.

Yet, apart from the conscientious objections of a sector of the population which was not condoning the new independence involving the departure of British forces, there was a show of warm cordiality in evidence for the forthcoming event. Not only from elements who would in any case welcome an end to British influence in Malta but also from others, including Britain herself.

There were days of activities and declarations being made in preparation for the approaching big day which government had already labelled as a date with destiny. With every day and activity filling a cog in the wheel that was turning towards a climax in which any grotesque shadows of failure had to be got away. Any restlessness that might have cropped up was dispelled by an atmosphere of rapidly growing trust and candour for all that was Maltese. There were boosting showmanship and activities in aid of the local arts – music, literature, painting and sculpture; there was emphasis made on workmanship and achievements, from the very first days of the nation. It was of course history and no one could turn it back. But in this, as many would have expected there was nothing which concerned ghosts. It was as if they had long been ostricized as having never belonged to history. If there was any mention of ghosts it was made only as an allegory of some service enjoyed in relation with British military presence which would now be no more.

But the kind of ghost being here referred to is like the one which Philippa and her family in the village of Żebbuġ had for many years been intermittently hearing making weird noises, unexplained footsteps and groaning loudly in their house. There had been periods when such manifestations would stop altogether almost cunningly whenever the family would decide to change house, only to start again after they would have succumbed to stay. It was now on the dawn of 1979 that there had been a relapse after a period of quiet. There were the noises and groans again, as well as articles which moved by themselves, and sometimes disappearing completely to reappear in a different place. They had never said anything about these manifestations to anyone as long as they remained in that house, but now that they managed to move to a new house the story was out.

A story of a different and certainly more mysterious nature emerged also during these hectic times. It concerned a family but particularly the daughter whom I am calling Elizabeth. It seemed that the father did not see eye to eye with his mother who had some time before went to Australia. Whatever effect there was from the mother and son estrangement must have been rightly or wrongly impinged on the daughter in such a way that she believed that her grandmother bore her ill will. Being young and carefree Elizabeth never bothered much about this, until one day she thought she noticed a change in a portrait of her grandmother which they had at home. Her first reaction was that she was imagining things, but on regarding the portrait longer and with more composure she became convinced of the look of hostility she saw in her grandmother's features which had not been there before. As she was retreating discomfited into another room she was sure that in a last glance she had at the picture there were the eyes moving as if to follow her departure with disapproval.

When she mentioned her experience there was amusement, alluding the incident to her imagination. If it wasn't this then it must have been some trick of the light on the portrait, said her father. But they were thrown into a pregnant silence, when on the following day they learned that the grandmother had passed away at about that same time Elizabeth had seen the movements in the portrait.

They had changed house then, perhaps for reasons other than occult, and with them went the portrait. But Elizabeth continued to avoid regarding it, particularly when she was alone. It still gave her the shivers, she said, as if even in the new place she still felt her grandmother's ghost about. One day however, as she happened to be looking into the well in their garden, she felt the presence of someone behind her, then there was the sensing of hands she could not see going round her waist to lift her, and push her into the well. She screamed and freed herself to run inside terrorized out of her wits.

She could of course have imagined it all. But there was certainly no imagination when whilst waiting on some friends who had come to see her father at home, she was discreetly asked by him to go upstairs to see about a door they heard opening. She returned to say that all doors were locked and that there was no one who could have opened them. Then before they knew what was happening the centre table and chairs in the sitting room where they were sitting began to elevate and float by themselves, with everyone who had witnessed the manifestation running like hell out of the room and the house.

Against the background of mechanics and causes that produced ghosts it was beyond anyone's ingenuity to explain the physical manifestations occurring in this case. There was certainly the poltergeistic element combining with something else. It could have been the ideal occasion for investigation and further enlightenment. But it wasn't the right time. Not for investigation anyway. It was the time however for ghosts to register their existence even in those times after belief in them had slipped out like air from a slow puncture. It was the time to establish that however lessened in manifestations for reasons which have already been explained, they had always held a place in history as they still merited to have in the new one that was being made.

The days were passing excitingly by, growing one by one into the beginnings of a past of important historical and social changes the import of which might after all disappear in the new future. But ghosts had formed a part of that past, as they indeed still belonged to the present. If there was any proof required this could be found amidst the hubbub for the approaching occasion – in the Presidential Palace of San Anton, where until some time back the noises and mysterious footsteps pertaining to the ghosts that haunted the place sixty years before, were still being heard.

Only a kind of lunatic illogic would ignore as much. But even if there were those who consciously or unconsciously were ignoring the ghosts of Malta as something non-existent or as being related to the fantasy of the few there was something happening in February 1979 as a sinister connotation of the fact.

This time it was an Englishman – one of the enchanted tourists that had by now began a regular exodus to the island. His name was Bill McGregor, a 44 year old from Hemel, Hempstead. It was expected that Mr McGregor would visit the old city of Mdina. All tourists do. It is the silent centuries old Siculo Norman city where one cannot help sensing the ghosts of the Arabs, Normans, Knights and of course Maltese that had thronged its narrow streets, even to this very day. Entering through the main gate into the city one is immediately held as if from the arm by Verdala Palace standing on its own on the right. This palace, dates back to the 15th century when it was the magisterial palace and law courts of the city. Beneath it there still lie the dungeons, as well as the chopping block where prisoners were executed by beheading. The horror of these underground chambers is belied by the restored edifice on top, and the beautiful courtyard embellished with greenery of all seasons. It was in fact this courtyard that attracted Mr McGregor, and seeing the orange trees laden with fruit, he decided to take a snap. It was just an ordinary instant camera he had to use which his wife had carried with her just for such an occasion. There was some characteristic balustrading in white Malta stone making a contrast with the green trees loaded with the luscious Maltese oranges. They would make the ideal picture to show to his grandchildren, thought Mr McGregor, and he took the snap.

But when the picture began to appear there seemed to be something on it which had definitely not been there when he took the snap. A few more seconds of concentration, and he realised that there had been an intruder in that picture.

Standing in front of the balustrading there was the figure of a headless girl, wearing a bridal gown.

The picture was examined by experts and declared to be genuine. They even went further to say that the figure seemed to be in chains, while one of her arms was crooked in a way as to indicate that she might have been holding her head in it, which did not appear in the picture. Both the story and the picture featured in English and Maltese newspapers as the possible headless bride of Medina. It was of course a title given by the English paper. Mr McGregor would not give one himself, because he was sceptical about ghosts. I don't know whether he still is.

There had never been offered any clue as to the origin of this haunting or the name of the haunter. Indeed this ghost had come to light for the first time through Mr McGregor's camera. It is of course easy to be blase in such cases and dismiss them by some uncommitting remark. But had anyone delved into historical records of those times he might have come across a small unimportant story of Katerina, a Maltese maiden of uncommon beauty, desired by a host of Knights whom she rejected in an act of faith towards her Maltese promised spouse. One of the Knights, more stubborn than the others accosted Katerina one day as her nuptials were drawing near, and tried on that occasion to take from her what she had solemnly promised only to her would-be spouse. The Knight would have succeeded had Katerina, pressed as she was to defend her virtue, not taken up the dagger he carried on his waist, and stabbed him to death. She was arrested, and it was now that her consistent refusals to compromise with the men who judged her when they had desired her, brought a similarily stubborn behaviour. She was condemned to death, but the court consented to Katerina's last wish of allowing her to marry her spouse before she was beheaded.

If this story were to be true, then she would have been beheaded just beneath where the ghost was photographed, and the other details of bridal gown, and chains could fit the story. Was this in fact the ghost of Katerina?

Whether it was or not there was certainly a fitting reminder and confirmation of the ghosts of Malta, coming at a time which was to remain as one of the most important in the island's history.

But the people were now more concerned with another approaching spectre which for better or for worse would certainly be haunting them in the future. The 31st March 1979 had arrived and the British military presence had to come to an end.

All British garrison establishments in Malta had closed down, and their personnel left quietly and sadly. There had only remained to effect the closing Rear-Admiral O.N.A. Cecil, the last Commander of British Forces in Malta, and Air-Commodore Hall, the last Air-Commander. The retinue was to be made by the 130 strong Salerno Marine Commando.

It was a parting between friends. This was evidenced not only during the last official functions with heads of both nationalities embracing and the audiences singing Auld Lang Syne, but also by the many spontaneous farewells given during those last days. On the appointed day of March 31st the ceremony of Independence was held at Vittoriosa, at the exact spot where the first British forces had come ashore in 1800. There had also been the last move out by the marines marching from Żabbar to Vittoriosa where they were to embark on the RFA logistics ship "Sir Lancelot." There were thousands of people watching them and waving their goodbyes along the route, but one in particular – 79 year old bemedalled Albert Gill, an ex naval man marched behind the contingent the whole way in a significant farewell. The last adieu was then on the morrow first given by Air-Commodore Hall as he circled low over Grand Harbour in a Nimrod, tipping the aircraft in salute to the President of the Republic who was with the crowds lining the ramparts along the harbour, to be followed by HMS London, with Rear Admiral Cecil on the bridge acknowledging the salutes from the President and the thousands with him.

It must have been a somewhat similar scene on 5th September 1800, when HMS Northumberland had entered that same harbour to give start to a new era. HMS London was now closing it. Malta had indeed emerged as a nation to go all along the ways of a new life, but it was never to be altogether detached from the main facts and factors imprinted in its history which might live for ever as ghosts of the past.

Even as this symbolic haunting was going on in Grand Harbour, there was another one, more real and significant going on in a building in Valletta which had for many years housed a minister during different legislatures. A member of the staff, going in on that day when the place was empty to check about the decorative lights that were to be put on at night could hear the noise of mysterious footsteps, and the banging of doors. He was by nature a sceptic and would not believe there was a ghost, even though he knew there was no one else in the building. But when the electricians he had to meet joined him, they too heard the ghostly noises and had the place checked inside out before they believed that what they were hearing was an unrestful spirit.

As they looked at each other not knowing what to say there reached them the sounds of cheering and shouting from the bastions and harbour nearby. There was then the roar of guns of HMS London firing a 21 gun salute – the last one to an island and people that were being left alone.

There was then no more firing or cheering to be heard, and a significant silence fell in that room. It was broken only by the repeated sound of ghostly footsteps – this time a little more hurried as if in anguish for something that had escaped away.

It was most of all in the way of contradiction that while the crowds outside were celebrating an occasion that was also supposed to pull the curtain down on ghosts, these were still active and lurking behind it. As if to continue in a perpetual conflict right into the new times.

Chapter 11

Judgement

Evening had come down on Malta and with it clouds and a biting wind carrying promise of rain. The bright day that thousands of tourists had witnessed during the morning as they paraded the streets of Valletta short sleeved and even half dressed had succumbed to the erratic wintry climate readily forecast by the Meteorological Office the night before hedging bets with the cautious prediction that there might after all possibly be rain. If it did come it would be a providential godsend and a heavenly reply to the prayers already being said in churches for the end of the drought and summery weather which had somehow been extending a Maltese summer right through autumn. In the same streets of Valletta, clerks from government offices, agency employees, secretaries, professional people, businessmen and salesgirls were hurrying to the bus terminus or to their private cars where they had them in parking places to reach home before the rain will come. A similar movement might have been evident in various parts of the island, this time with workers from factories, drydocks and other industrial areas. Two hours later the whole position would be reversed with an exodus of people from home making a bee-line for places of entertainment, rain or no rain. They would go to theatres, discos and similar places. Cars will now be more in evidence in the brightly illuminated streets, with their vividly coloured bodies glistening. For those who will not go out there will be the television with some seven stations to choose from the local and Italian network to entertain them right into the night.

This was Malta in 1979. A far cry from the days described in the first chapter of this work from which the island was now obviously differing by far more than mere time or distance. It had been a run for achievement with a thirty five year intervening period of what could be described as domestic squabbling rather than strife by two political factions on which the people were more or less equally divided, with each side taking turns to run the five year legislatures and leaving its imprint in particular contributions to the making of the nation of to-day.

Between them they had moulded the future they wanted. They had not only changed the face of the land in what constituted buildings and roads but also the ways of life relating to work, social conditions, food, and leisure. There had also been the development of new mental aptitudes which produced the economic miracle and the emergence of a new generation. They had however retained, even if this was in the form of a riddle, much of what was always intrinsically Maltese in character and tradition. More fatefully enigmatic than this riddle of tradition there is the awesome and fantastic drama of ghosts.

When life was simple and bereft of intelligence and dexterity acquired in the latest years, ghosts constituted a most devastating element in Maltese existence. They were rooted and basic, forming part of the very structure of society. And because they were thus embedded and representing that which was only Maltese in history, religion, life and custom that they earned the unique qualification of being the ghosts of Malta. Now this seems to be no more. Because of a materialistic trend which allows no quarter where no ready scientific explanation is available. So the ghosts of Malta although still undenied remain also unconfirmed. When in this time of progress everything is being examined and dissected to get to the bottom of things in a spirit of leaving no secrets or explanations to be given in doubtful undertones, ghosts are being left in suspense. Maybe the time has come for an independent judgement to be given.

If there is to be such a judgement, consideration will have to be taken of all the manifestations which have since time immemorial been taking place. Particularly during the last thirty five years when the Maltese knew better than to rest on the element of hallucination or folklore as they were imbued with new knowledge. It was incidentally the same knowledge that had already failed to find an explanation for the incidence of ghosts elsewhere. But it is not only the stories, however authentic, that will have to decide the issue. There are the explanations proposed for the possibility of the psyche to function after the body's death as it had done in life. And this is something which enjoys a distinct advantage in Malta through belief because of faith in the spirit's survival after bodily death.

An important point for the ghosts of Malta lies in the face that they had existed right through the country's history. Theirs was a story to be relayed throughout times to various audiences with similarily different states of mind. This in itself rules out the imaginary element to bring in the one constant factor of the reality status by persisting right through the years to these very days. On the other hand, it would be inconceivable to reconcile the Malta of to-day with innovations in the way of development that can be seen and touched with manifestations by the psyche to return to its scenes of human participation of hundreds of years ago. Yet, with all the arguments to discredit the past and dismiss its ghosts as myths, we have seen these ghosts persisting in our times. Even as the tarmac roads took over from the old thoroughfares, the new buildings continued to swamp the old, and the traditional that was to stay was being touched up and brought to scratch to fit the new times, there was still active beneath the new layers being laid that something of the old which had not been suppressed.

This could have been the right time for a revival; when history that was being made was seen to be still teeming with the ghosts it had always carried. But there was still no hint of any attempt at this.

Truly enough there were now the first domestic troubles to alienate the new republic making its first steps on its new road, alone. There had been the heavy rains that had caused damage and loss of life. Fields were flooded and crops that were destroyed. More than any interest in psychic manifestations one might have expected there was the preoccupation about a possible comeback of the cattle disease that had already ravaged the livestock herd the year before. There were also the hundred and one other things to be seen to, and to deviate the Maltese with their trait of unification in face of need from ethereal ghosts. Maybe after these teething troubles were over there would be time for them.

But there was still no change. On the contrary, with the dawn of 1980 there was more of the inescapable logic of dwindling belief in anything remaining in the curriculum of life other than work, industrialisation, export, tourism, political and financial stability and similar endeavours. Recognition of phenomenal experience became a non-entity. For the majority of public opinion ghosts were doomed.

After centuries full of fantastic ghosts to enliven a country's history this seemed to be a depressing conclusion. If there was any hope it was to be found only in the way of a compromise, leaving everyone to his own opinion. Indeed to-day in Malta there are the sceptics, the disbelieving, and those who cannot be bothered with ghosts and their stories. But there are also those who directly or indirctly have come in contact with them and are living witnesses to their existence. History and ghosts seem to be set on a separate way of their own with each side sticking to its part in the existing compromise that everyone is very much alive to.

Whether or not accepting the premise of ghosts and haunting however one cannot afford to ignore the reached stage of such phenomena. In the absence of their proper study this might provide ground for the long awaited decision. As fate would have it there was at this very time an extraordinary case happening which was particularly interesting because of its factual and verifiable detail.

It began with a business deal – one of the many then going on as if to boost hope and confidence in a still unknown future. It was a take-over of a printing press, with one owner transferring his business to another, lock stock and barrel, including the employees to run it. Ralph (as I am calling him) who was the new owner was an enterprising young man of the new generation eager to have a go at business, and was more than convinced of his success. There was only one snag he wanted to get fixed. One of his employees who was the most senior, he noticed, was given a wide berth by his mates. This was not in line with his project; he wanted a happy team. So by putting a word here and there he got to know the reason behind it. This man was reputed to have the evil eye. It was a laughing matter and Ralph tried to laugh it off. Even when this worker warned another to beware of a traffic accident which indeed happened as he had hinted. When he warned another worker about working in the dark room there was the lamp going off as he had forecast; something it had never done before. A joking remark from him concerning a milk bottle immediately sent the bottle crashing to the floor to be smashed into smithereens. These might have been considered small things and were somehow tolerated. But when the machinery began to be involved Ralph became worried. He could not understand how a press left in working order the last thing at night should be out of order on the start of morning work. When he could stick it no longer he had this worker sacked.

The first day when the press had to do without him was a day like any other. Only that some orders for work were cancelled. Then things began to go wrong. Bad workmanship became the order of the day calling for redoing with loss of time and money. Apart from reflecting badly on the firm. Orders then stopped coming in, until there came a day when the firm had nothing to do.

A week or two of this made a drain on capital, and when the situation persisted Ralph got rattled. He was convinced there was something wrong. Only that he did not know what it was. He had recourse to several friends without success. Until one suggested that he should get a priest to exorcise for any evil cast on the place. Ralph was inclined to laugh this off too. He did not believe in spells or the evil eye, if that was what his friend was saying. But there was more than that in what was being hinted. When evil spirits were mentioned it occurred to Ralph that they had gone out of fashion with the new nation and the generation to which he belonged. But failing any other way out of his impasse he decided to do what he was told.

In Malta there are more priests than one could care for, and Ralph knew many of them. But to his astonishment none of them could find the time to do what he asked. All seemed to have been particularly occupied. It began to seem to him that the spell or whatever it was that was cast on his business covered this angle as well. He was now convinced that what he had to fight against was of an occult nature. More than rattled he became terrified, and this made him run faster from one priest to another even to those he did not know until he found one who was ready to help him. It was agreed to have Mass said in the premises during which there will also be said prayers for exorcism. All the employees would attend and the appointment was made for the first public holiday which happened to be the 1st May 1980.

It was a new experience for Ralph, always an unbeliever in ghosts. This applied also to his employees who were all of the same generation to which the occult did not appeal. As the Mass proceeded with nothing unusual occurring Ralph began to feel frustrated. He began thinking that he might after all have been a fool to take the suggestion. But whatever unworthy thoughts he was having were suddenly arrested when there was the beginning of a commotion. It began as the celebrant came to consecrate the host. There was first the rattling of the three doors to the building as if by a wind. But there was no wind blowing on that day. There was neither any one pushing those doors as one of them was open and everyone could see there was nobody near it.

All eyes were now on the doors as the shaking and rattling continued and became more vigorous as the priest carried on with the service. The poor man had gone white with fear, and all could see that he was trembling all over. To his credit goes the fact that he did not falter, as he must have found sustenance in the consecrated host which he began raising for adoration. It was here that there was a noticeable factor. As he raised the host the door just opposite to where he looked would stop shaking, only to start again as the host was lowered. The climax of the drama was reached however when the priest began to recite the prayers for exorcism. It was now that hell was let loose. The doors began to shake with a tremendous din. It was as if a herd of elephants on stampede was at them. Even the walls of the building seemed to tremble. As the priest continued with the prayers barely audible in the din all those inside knew that the dialogue of prayer and the devilish manifestation had become like a test of strength in a combat between good and evil. Then suddenly the shaking and the din stopped and silence fell on the place like a blanket. The combat was over. More than the silence there was a strange feeling of peace which as Ralph and his employees said had never been felt before. It continued in the days that followed.

For those who might have thought of this as a likely starter for a come-back there were false hopes. It had now become common knowledge that attempts to impress or influence the sceptical had become like those of someone fated to be climbing an endless sand dune of shifting sands, making little or no headway before slipping back to pause and think of trying again the futile upward climb. This had become more than a simple allegory. A few weeks later there was still another case to prove it. It was on 20th June, to be exact. The radio and newspapers were in the morning flashing the story of the spectre of a nun which had appeared at a popular beach in Sliema carrying two dogs in her arms. She had then gone across the water to the other side like a Christ on the water of Genesareth, to re-appear at a school and terrorize children. There was the expected hubbub at the news, so characteristic of the Maltese, but only to subside as quickly as it had arisen. No amount of statements from fishermen hospitalized for fright, or children who would not speak for shok, would persuade a majority by now seemingly turned for ever sceptic. The following day was like any other. The weather was beautiful as always, with a bright sun in a clear sky. A soft breeze arose to temper the first day of summer with a sense of delicate felicity. And the people went on with their business of living.

No more stories however spectacular would deviate them from such business which had now become their contribution to a country trying to hold its own in a world building into an impasse. With enough suffocating air around, in which every country was voicing its anguish at being caught in the cogs of a pitiless economic machine. Theirs was a nation with many others caught in a dark world demanding a drastic remedy to an oil question, mass unemployment and a mad race in prices. On their agenda there was also the wanting of a virile attempt to halt the forces that were making for war.

These were the tenets of the new nation. They could be translated into a sound explanation for excluding all that had no direct contribution for the common effort. With a people that were now wont to put aside all that is not a task to be undertaken. But very often men with such a god's sight may after all be human-blind.

It is one thing to take together as one whole the endeavours being made in the various sectors. But it is another to take them individually. History, culture, reconstruction, industrialisation, employment, tourism, housing and many other factors. Trying to absorb them all at once tends to leave one dazzled and breathless leaving no place or time for anything else. But if they are taken slowly, one by one, then each picture begins to make sense for its proper fitting into the big mosaic wherein may lie the important clue for the question of ghosts which is to be judged. The preservers of history had managed to retain all the historical and cultural elements of Verdala Castle when some time ago it was given a new look and turned into a VIP reception quarter. It was made to fit the new times and receive heads of state as befitting the new nation. any stories about its being haunted had long been shed away. Yet, this did not stop two soldiers on duty there recently from finding themselves in situations that were inexplicable by natural laws and which could very well be attributed to occult influences. The only possible explanation that was forthcoming was that what occurred had happened when they were in the room once reputably haunted by the Blue Lady. One cannot fail to mention as one of the feats of reconstruction the transfromation effected to the civil airport at Luqa. Arrival and departure lounges have been remade to take the bigger air traffic and more passengers, whilst the airfield was endowed with a new runway to take jumbo jets. However, no dog would approach the spot still reputed to be haunted by the ghost of a crashed pilot of the last war. There is the house in the village of Żebbuġ which must have undergone several proceses of reconstructon since it original days over a hundred years ago. Yet it had never given up its ghost. All the members of the family still witness the occasional replay of a priest hurtling himself from a roof into a well in the internal courtyard. Just as he had done a hundred years back.

One of the most recent masterpieces in culture of the new Malta is without any doubt the Mediterranean Conference Centre in Valletta. It is a gem of a place beautifully restored from the Sacra Infermeria of the Knights of St John, which was built in 1574 during the grandmastership of Jean de la Cassiere. It had in 1676 become a teaching hospital with its own school of anatomy and surgery which was then established by the Grandmaster of the time Nicolas Cottoner. It had then continued to be used as a hospital by both French and British until 1920, when it was turned into a Police Headquarters until the outbreak of World War Two in 1939. In its new livery as one of the best Conference Centres in Europe it now hosts conferences at international level. But its spacious halls are also used for exhibitions, and its auditorium as a theatre which has also hosted the Black and White Minstrel Show. Yet, a gracious first lady says that she cannot bear the sense of coldness and foreboding every time she has to sit there for some function. It is, and here I am quoting her, as if beneath the magnificence of the building there still lurk the active spirits from history of those who might have died there and left their imprinted influence notwithstanding the passage of time and the renovations carried out.

In the same way as these stories are hushed, reliable voices confirm by discreet word or remark that palaces of the Knights are still haunted. In the course of rebuilding, demolished houses are still occasionally unearthing remains of those whose ghosts they had borne. If these ghosts now haunt no more it is only in confirmation of a fact. Until these very days no new factory or enterprise is started unless it is blessed by a priest. As if the old belief deep in folk memory still stirs, notwithstanding the new times and emancipated people. While all this is going on, the Church still watches over this most catholic of countries without every denying the stories of this and that having made an appearance from another existence. Ask the tourist who snapped the Medina ghost, or the other who from his hotel window witnessed the drama of the spectral nun gliding over the waters of Sliema. Their answers will take one back to the middle ages when ghosts roamed at random. All this has been happening now when a new Malta is still rising up. Not only allegorically, in maturity and ideals, but also materially in new towns and landscape. A landscape of modern white stone buildings that remains pock-marked with old grey structures still closed and abandoned when the space they occupy is so badly wanted. Because they are the mute accomplices of the ghosts of Malta.

Chapter 12

Ghosts of the Eighties and the Nineties

It seems that if a stage for judgement and compromise on the matter of ghosts might have been reached in the beginning of the eighties, this had still to be revised. Because much as the hurrying years had continued to bring changes to Malta and her people in the social, political and other progressive fields, there has been no change neither in the interest nor incidence of ghosts.

It is true that the fast rate of progress might have alienated public opinion and entrenched it in more materialistic fields than that of ghosts. But by no stretch of imagination can one believe that these have fizzled out, and it can be said that after the publication and outright sale of the first edition of this book on ghostly manifestations right on to the threshold of the eighties, it has not been found difficult to trace more manifesting ghosts of various types right into and towards the close of this decade. This should strengthen the argument in confronting sceptics and those who have been postponing their belief in ghosts until they see one, that this element of the occult is not the figment of imagination they make it to be. And this is amply substantiated by the new cases being mentioned in the following pages.

Bur Marrad is a small village to be reached from the town of Mosta on the way to St.Paul's Bay. It is nothing to shout about, but it radiates a feeling that notwithstanding what development began to take place, the village still retains an individual character with its placid pastoral landscape and way of life. Its people still belong to their countryside much as do the numerous farms and vineyards, hiding streams, meadows and an expanse of countryside that add to the flavour of a mellow world and landscape. Yet, behind it all, the village also has a ghost.

I was told about it by a man called John who after reading my first book was one of the many who came forward with the latest information about ghostly manifestations. John told me of the occasion when he was motoring with his friend Paul who was driving. They had just left St.Paul's Bay on their way to Mosta when on reaching the main road at Bur Marrad just past the church which splits the motorway they saw an old man in the middle of the road. He seemed to be in no hurry to cross and just stood looking at the car as if impervious to the danger of being hit. Paul slowed down and stopped near the man to ask him if he wanted a lift. But there was no reply and the old man just looked blankly at Paul as if not understanding what was being said to him. So they drove on. But they had hardly gone twenty metres or so when they saw the old man again right in the middle of the road in front of them as before. This time Paul did not stop, but swerved to avoid him and drove on.

"That was strange, wasn't it?" said John .

"I would say it was," answered Paul.

There was more that John wanted to say to Paul but did not utter another word as he saw his friend changing gear rapidly and pressing hard on the accelerator to increase speed, and indeed they were soon driving faster as if the devil himself was on their tail.

"Paul, why are you driving so fast? Do you want to get us both killed?" said John to his friend.

But Paul seemed that he had not heard him and continued on their way with his foot pressed right down on the accelerator as if trying to get the most out of the engine. And what further pleas were made by John to slow down went unheeded.

It was only when they reached Mosta that Paul stopped the car, and began to regain his composure after the look of apprehension that had been on his face.

"Now, can you tell me what happened to you Paul?" asked John.

"Why were you going so dangerously fast?"

"It was that old man," replied Paul. "Didn't you see him?"

"Of course I did, and twice on the road at Bur Marrad."

"No," said Paul. "It's not that. After we saw him the second time and I drove on, in the next instant I saw him in the driving mirror, and he was sitting in the back seat, right behind us. He only disappeared when we reached here."

Who was the ghostly hitch-hiker? And why were these two men the only motorists to collect this phantom? Because they were sure he was one.

The next protagonist to come forward was George. This is not his real name which I was asked not to reveal, but what he had to say is more interesting since he is an Englishman although the son of a Maltese mother. It was after reading my book that he got in touch with me from England where he lives to tell me of the fantastic experiences he had in Malta.

It was expected that after he and his brother whom I am calling Tom had finished a working assignment away from home, their mother who was then staying in Malta would ask them to spend a holiday here. Both of them arrived on the evening of 4th November, 1980, and from the airport they drove straight to a house in Rudolph Street, Sliema which their mother had leased and made ready for them. The two happy-go-lucky lads were in the best of spirits with straying thoughts about painting the town red on their first night here. But these thoughts had to be surrendered to a more pressing feeling of exhaustion which made them change their mind. So discarding even the first essential of unpacking their luggage they went straight to bed. But even with the state he was in, George could not sleep. He attributed this to his spending the first night in new surroundings, and he found confirmation when he heard the steady footsteps along the corridor outside his room which persisted throughout the night and made him conclude that Tom must have also been having a bout of insomnia. However, when he mentioned the matter to him in the morning Tom said that he had not left his bed during that night, and having also heard the footsteps he had thought it was him who had been walking about.

Nothing more was said about the matter as the two brothers set about to unpack their luggage. Tom started with some photos and postcards he always carried with him, and which he began sticking round the mirror on his dressing table. However, as soon as he turned round to see to the rest of his luggage one of the pictures flew out from the mirror right onto his face. The two brothers looked at each other in disbelief, but then on remembering the strange footsteps they had heard that night they realized there must have been a ghost in that house. Their first reaction was to joke about the matter. So much so that Tom suggested they should try and find out whether the haunting ghost was a male or female. Therefore before leaving the house that morning to go and see their mother they left a magazine on Tom's bed, opened on an irrelevant page, thinking however lightly that it would attract the ghost's attention, and to their amazement it did for when they returned home later in the morning, although the magazine was still where they had left it, it had been turned to another page with a full picture of a nude woman. More than confirming that there was a ghost in the house, this made them conclude it was a male.

When told about these occurrances their mother was not surprised and she told them how when she had gone to clean the place before their arrival she had been mysteriously thrown down some stairs. She was nonetheless perturbed because she concluded the ghost must have been a violent poltergeist. She suggested that the boys should leave that house and go to stay with her, but they were adamant since by now they were looking at the whole thing as an adventure. They even began to take more interest and were soon associating the haunting with a trapdoor there was on the ceiling which could be reached by the spiral staircase where their mother had been thrown. George told me that the sinister looking heavily bolted trapdoor was like what was used on a gallows, and he was continuously looking at it expecting to see a body swinging from it.

But nothing like this happened. Instead on the following night Tom had to find refuge beneath his bed covers, one moment listening to the footsteps in the corridor, and then to a scratching right over his head. When these manifestations failed to bring a reaction from him, before dawn came he was subjected to a trauma of a choking sensation when invisible hands began pressing on his throat. When this too was over, contrary to the fall in temperature persons feel when in the grip of a ghostly manifestation, Tom was suddenly feeling very hot, and this even though the weather was wintry cold that day.

The rest of their second day in that place was full of manifestations. They were minor ones which are normally associated with an annoying poltegeist like electricity switches shutting off and coming on again by themselves, windows sticking for no apparent reason, and both lads hearing quite clearly their name being called and recognising each other's voice. They were small things indeed which however were building up to a climax which came in the early hours of the following day.

It was five in the morning when Tom sat up in his bed and lit a cigarette. Suddenly there appeared in his room a misty white figure hovering a foot or so above the floor. It was the figure of a young person more like a child which seemed to be in a lying position. Tom stood petrified where he was, pulling quickly at his cigarette until the ghostly apparition floated towards the closed door of the room to be sucked under and disappear. With it also disappeared Tom's resistance, and he jumped out of his bed and ran to George's room shouting that he had seen the ghost. After it was dawn both of them left the house. They went there again only to take out their belongings when they were met by tremendous vibrations of the trapdoor in the ceiling as if what devilish force there was behind it wanted to get at them. When they took what they wanted they left quickly never to return there again.

It was easy to find this haunted house from the information given to me by George. When I found it I was told it was uninhabited. But on looking at one of the windows I got a glimpse of a face that moved quickly out of sight. It could have been my imagination, but I don't think so. And I still remember the fleeting impression I had of the face of a young man, distorted by a look of pain and anguish. As there would have been on the face of the youth who, I was told, had hanged himself in that house some thirty years before.

This one was a good example of a poltergeist which the Germans call a noisy ghost, as in fact the word means. There have already been mentioned several manifestations by this type of ghost in Malta and as can be seen they still exist. More than being just noisy I would say that poltergeists are more often than not vindictive since being restless spirits they tend to annoy and harass mortals they come across. There was a more recent one located at a restaurant in St.Paul's Bay. Run by a foreigner the place began doing good business but when management and employees began to be harassed by this ghost they had to give up and the place was closed down.

In a previous chapter there have already been explained the mechanics of manifestations whose consistency is believed to be ectoplasm activated by a charge of energy which may fluctuate in force and on this will depend whether the haunting spirit takes form as a fully fledged ghost or is restrained to be active as a white and cottony substance or vapour obviously derived from the elements of ectoplasm. Hauntings by these types of ghosts were always rife in Malta. They must have reduced since as I already had occasion to explain the generated energy tends to weaken and these hauntings stand to disappear by time. Yet it seems that the eighties can still claim to produce such hauntings and not very long ago I got to know of one which occurred at Paola.

My informant was Mark, a young and sober lad who every evening or occasionally a bit later had to pass through an ordinary narrow street on his way home. This lies in the vicinity of St.Ubaldesca Church and incidentally quite close to Arcade Street where I was first introduced to the world of ghosts as already mentioned in one of the first chapters of this book. But that was more than forty years ago. The manifestation I am recounting occurred in the mid-eighties. Mark had been through that street for years, and there was never anything unusual. There was enough time for him to notice the progress in rebuilding a bombed site which was a relic of the last war and where three persons had been killed. It was well after the demolished buildings were completely reconstructed and inhabited that the ghost struck.

Mark was walking along the street as usual when suddenly he became aware that there was something sinister in the air. At first it was only a feeling and he tried to shake it off. But then he began to have a sensation of coldness. Although he did not then know such a sensation was a general characteristic in hauntings, he somehow began to associate it with a ghostly manifestation. So he tried to run along the rest of the street but to his amazement found himself rooted to the spot, and by now paralyzed with terror. The next moment he could sense rather than see some dense concoction in the air which he felt rolling closer with intensification of the cold sensation, and then before he knew it this was all around him as a vapour and he was soon enveloped in the cold, clammy substance which gave him the worst fright of his life. It was only his sense of survival that made him scream, and then to his relief he found his feet again and began running, to stop only when he reached home. I don't know whether this manifestation happened to anyone else. Mark too, cannot help me, because he never went through that street again. But till to-day he trembles when talking about that never-to-be-forgotten experience.

Much as I had researched this book and written it in good faith, I will not be surprised if sceptics may still find it difficult to accept my judgement and believe what I have uncovered. I have no quarrel with such people, as after all I hold no brief for ghosts and my only interest is their history once thought to be a legacy of the past but now proving itself to be also something we have to live with in our times and also those of the future. However should there be those seeking more independent proof or confirmation of a haunting, the case that follows may be what they want. Gentlemen of the press are usually a little sceptical of anything which cannot be photographed or persuaded to give them an interview. But they are always sensitive to the unusual and quick to react to it. And indeed it was the press which unearthed my next ghost without my knowing or having to do anything about it, and the manifestation was witnessed not by one person but by a crowd. The story was reported in the *Weekend Chronicle* of 4th June, 1983 and I am reproducing it faithfully as it appeared.

> "Joseph Attard, the author of the current best-seller THE GHOSTS OF MALTA, insists in his book that reports of ghost-sightings have dwindled more due to Modern Man's lack of enthusiasm for anything spiritual rather than any real shortage of ghosts. The shortage is purely artificial, he writes, and a group of theatre enthusiasts now seem all set to back him.... a Sliema Hotliner has phoned to say that members of the AST A Tijatru group at the Tigne Art complex have actually witnessed a ghost during recent rehearsals of Kafka's "Metamorfożi". The ghost has been described as that of a young man who was first heard whining in a corner of the tower. The rehearsal was abandoned but resumed later in the week, although some members have refused to set foot in there again. But producer Michael Fenech (not one for gimmicks, so forget any such suspicion) stuck to his guns.... will keep you informed of the Tigne Ghost."

All I can add to the above is that after investigations I found out that a young man had met his death after a fall at that place and it must have been his ghost that was seen on the mentioned occasion.

Another newspaper, this time the Chronicle and Echo brought forth another Malta haunting in its issue of 30th October, 1983. The story concerned Cyril and Sheila Greaves of Northampton who were holidaying in Malta, who after one of their many enjoyable but hectic days returned to their hotel a traditional edifice in the northern part of the island and which was more than 100 years old. On going to bed both of them dropped off like a log, but some time later in the night Sheila woke up to go to the toilet. Only that there was a sinister looking green light on the door of their room which puzzled her. She stopped and waited as if to see what was happening but when she saw the light getting bigger and more phosphorous she became scared. She tried to wake up her husband, but as the light had then disappeared Cyril didn't bother and just rolled over to continue with his sleep. In the morning the matter seemed to have been forgotten, and Cyril might have even concluded that his wife had only had a bad dream. But when their holiday came to an end, before leaving the hotel Cyril took a picture of their room with an ordinary camera, and when the film was developed after their return to England there was the evidence to see that his wife had after all been right about what she saw in the hotel room at Malta. For the picture he had taken of their room showed a ghastly bearded face of a man in the spot where she had seen the light on the door. This picture was also carried with the feature in the newspaper.

This was a haunting of the Materialization type in which the ghost assumes the actual appearance of a representation of its form occupied during life. I had included another manifestation of this type in this book where a headless bride appeared in a garden at Rabat. As coincidence would have it this was also discovered through a picture taken by two English tourists and was similarly reported by a newspaper in England. Ghosts in this category of manifestation are often motionless and noiseless while they emit neither any sense of evil nor violence. On the contrary the next two cases to be mentioned and which I investigated personally both carry a diabolical element, and both occurred at the bedside of moribund persons. In the first case a gentleman I know and whom I have no reason to disbelieve told me how when on the point of death he saw four devils at his bedside. He told me this of course after he recovered. I don't exclude that his was only a hallucination resulting from the state that he was in when it happened, but although understanding such possibility himself, this gentleman still insists that he had seen the devils. So I think I'd better leave it at that. The other case is different and it concerned another gentleman who more than a friend was related to me. So much so I was several times at his bedside during his last days and I was much impressed with his tranquility and resignation in meeting death which he knew was aproaching. When the end was near he was surrounded by his family, including his son who came over from the United States together with his Portuguese wife. During his last moments he seemed to be hypnotized and was oblivant of all the people that were around him when suddenly he let out a piercing scream and shouted "Ma".

His wife and all those that were in the room thought that he was calling his mother. But after he died and his son returned to the United States, his wife told him how when his father had screamed she saw a lion at the foot of his bed. One cannot then but conclude that it was that which made him utter the word "Ma" which in Malta is also an expression of fear. If this was so, and I have no reason to believe it wasn't, then the apparition must have been diabolical rather than that of a ghost. This happened in 1986. Since then, the widow who I personally know to be very sensitive to ghostly manifestations, tells me that she still feels the presence of her dead husband in the house which only manifests itself in the form of a sense of peace and contentment that exists in that house.

This brings us to another alleged supernatural element wherein it is believed that although certain spirits do not manifest themselves they seem to exert control on the atmosphere of a place. It sometimes happens that when going into a building one may sense a sympathetic ambience. On the other hand a building may radiate an unfriendly feeling or even downright evil. I met many people who had experienced this, but I might have found a good example in a palatial edifice which was built in 1562–64. In the course of time this building passed to a number of successive owners, members of the Maltese nobility. There was a time when the place was also used as a school, but since some years ago it has been used as a health spot and patronized by foreign guests seeking a healthy diet, exercise and a quiet holiday. !t is a beautiful place with a style of architecture enhanced by the mellow globigerina limestone used in its constructuion. The wooden beamed ceiling in rooms overlooking a patio shaded by orange trees depict a setting reminescent of another era. But the most striking effect made on whoever stays in that place is the overwhelming aura of calmness and well-being it sheds.

According to the lady who runs it the place is well patronized by guests who never fail to return year after year, all being attracted by its powerful atmosphere of warmth and comfort which she attributes to some supernatural element. Yet the place never had a ghost. However there was a possible meaning of her belief when one of her guests who happened to be a clair-voyant sensed the presence of good and quiet spirits in the various rooms of the palace and he offered to substantiate what he said by drawing their portraits through his psychic powers. He did indeed produce these portraits which have been included in this book.

I am unable to say whether these portraits really depict spirits that are still impinged in that palace which at some time was their earthly habitat, or were only the fruit of a fertile imagination of a good artist. It must however be said that the clairvoyant who drew them was on his first visit to Malta and had no previous knowledge of the palace and much less of its inhabitants throughout the last 500 years. Moreover it will be noticed that one of the portraits shows its subject wearing a military uniform of his time, and indeed one of the family's ancestors who once owned and lived in that palace was a colonel. Then there is what the lady who runs it told me that after checking with a still living descendant of the family she was told that the portrait of the lady who the clairvoyant found impinged in the room that was in its time the chapel, bears a marked resemblance to a member of the family who had indeed lived in that palace.

It cannot be denied that the ghosts of Malta may after all also strike a positive note for the local economy with the popularity they enjoy amongst tourists and other curious foreigners. In this regard this book may even be considered as a supplement to the more tangible attractions which Malta has to offer. One cannot of course rule out the occasional negative effect resulting from some hauntings as it appeared to have been the case with a ghost I was told about recently.

The story came from a small fishing village, until some years ago one of the few remaining spots retaining the character and environment of a restful holiday resort largely sought by summer residents. The wave of progress has however changed all this and the increased population in this village with the influx of more tourists has been calling for more amenities and entertainment. It was against this background of rushed improvements that an entrepreneur obtained permission to build a place of entertainment at a spot where an old small church had lain closed and derelict for may years and was demolished. Permission was given with the condition that there would be no desecration of a grave there had been in the church which held the remains of an old priest who had been its chaplain. The work was taken in hand and progress was made until the workers came to open the grave so as to remove the bones that were in it and give them an alternative burial. But much as they tried to remove the slabs which covered the grave, they couldn't do it. There weren't any apparent difficulties, while the men were skilled workers with the right tools. But, as one of them told me, as soon as they would manage to lever out a slab this would fall back in place as if pulled by some supernatural force from the grave. Some of the workers left, but the entrepreneur, not to be thwarted by any ghost took a bulldozer and removed the slabs in no time. It must have seemed to him that he had won this round, but I was informed that the ghost had his own in the next when after the establishment was ready and opened for business it lacked patronage as if after having lost the fight through manifestations the ghost had now laid a curse on the place.

It was only recently that I went to see this place. My intention was to see the owner and get the real story from him, but I found it closed and through some apertures where glass in doors and windows was broken I could see that the interior was in shambles with roofs and floors having been removed, while some scaffolding and cleanly cut stone on the outside might have meant that the place was being reconstructed from scratch. On one of the walls there was still stuck a menu list, but what struck me as being more significant of the story was the still standing signboard done in glass and neon tubing with the name of the place "the Ghost Busters Bar". This might have been initially chosen to show that the owner had won his fight with the ghost, but it was also in the way of confirmation that such a ghost had really existed. Whether it had indeed been subdued will be known later if and when the place is reconstructed.

Having mentioned so many cases of ghostly manifestations in Malta up to the end of the eighties it is not to be understood that these had stopped by the end of that period. Indeed, interest in this subject continued and I came across several manifestations that occurred in the nineties. I was told of one particular case which had actually occurred in the seventies but came to light only recently as the person who had witnessed it kept it to himself because nobody would believe him. He only related it to me recently as he thought I would understand. As a matter of fact, I did not. But because of the peculiarity of the case I felt I had to mention it in this new edition of my work. Mario is a well known gentleman in Balzan; a well educated and sober person who has no time for fantasy or wild stories. He had never believed in ghosts, and much less dabbled in their manifestations until one day in the seventies he had an extraordinary manifestation at his home in Balzan. His wife had gone out shopping, and as usual he remained at home watching television while his toddler son stayed with him playing with his pet dog. Suddenly, there was an unusual flash on the TV screen, and there was the figure of a man emerging from that screen. Head, torso, arms and legs came out until there was the complete virile figure of a man who went gliding swiftly to one side of the room, because he had no feet. Mario was flabbergasted and could not utter the exclamation of fear that came to his mouth. For a second he might have thought he was dreaming. But such a thought was quickly dispelled when his son went running after the ghostly figure followed by the dog also barking at the spectre in the way that had been mentioned before with dogs being very sensitive of ghosts. This episode ended when the ghost disappeared. I had never known of any manifestation like this, and truly enough it was very hard to believe. But then I could not disbelieve Mario.

A clearcut manifestation of the nineties came from an English lady who after reading my book in England thought it fit to write to me about her experience while she was on one of her frequent visits to Malta in 1993. On that occasion she was staying with a Maltese friend of hers at Qormi, when one night whilst going to the toilet she was shocked out of her senses on seeing an old man sitting in an armchair. Any thoughts that she was imagining it all were dispelled when as she went past, the old man raised the cap he was wearing in salute. She was of course terrified and dreaded the moment when she had to go back to her bedroom. But when she did, she was relieved to see that the armchair was empty, and that the old man was gone. In the morning she told her friend what had happened, and on being asked to describe the man she mentioned how he was wearing a boldly checked shirt, a white scarf and of course the cap. Her friend immediately replied that her description matched that of her dead father, adding that the white scarf must have been the towel which he used to wear round his neck for the sweat. Moreover, she did not seem to have been surprised, because, as she said, she had long felt his presence in the house persisting after his death. The story did not end there, because after returning to England the English lady related everything to her husband and tried to show him a picture of her friend's father which she had with other pictures in a drawer. This was indeed a photo of the old man's picture inserted on his tomb stone in Malta. To their amazement however, when she got the picture they found out that the face had completely vanished. Even after what had happened, this lady did not jump to any conclusions and had another picture made form the negative she had. This second picture turned out well, but some time later the face began to get blurred again, to vanish completely later on.

Although I was asked for an explanation, I had none to give for this particular manifestation. It was after all like many others that were featured in this book. One may find a possible scope or reason for haunting only if it is not hushed up and is investigated. These two elements then, very aptly bring me to an interesting haunting which was made public and to a certain extent investigated in 1996.

The ghost in his haunting is presumed to be that of Sir Oliver Starkey, a senior Knight of the Order of St. John. The story of this knight takes us back in history to 1558 when Queen Elizabeth I had acceded to the English throne and tried to start a recovery of the Order of St. John in England where it had been suppressed. But this did not materialize and by 1560 the British Langue of the Order had dwindled to only two knights – Sir Oliver Starkey and James Shelley. Both of these left England and came to Malta. It was then that Grandmaster Jean Parisot de la Vallette took Starkey as his secretary and confidante. It is not surprising then that when Valletta was built he had a house of his own constructed in the city, where it still stands to-day in Merchants Street. The English knight played a very important part in the Great Siege of 1565 and lived to serve with distinction under three other grandmasters after

La Vallette, i.e. Pietro del Monte, Jean l'Evaque de la Cassiere and Hugues de Verdalle known as Verdala. Starkey died in 1588 at the age of 63, and because of the part he played in the Order he was buried in the crypt of St. John's Co-Cathedral, a stone's throw away from his house.

This house became derelict for many years until in 1987 it was bought by the Russian government, and after restoration and refurbishment, was established as a Russian Cultural Centre in 1990. What happened after that was then made public in *The Times* (of Malta) of 10th September, 1996.

We were told that it was at the beginning of 1993 that Dr. Elizavetta Zolina, the Centre's director and her husband began hearing strange noises during the night. These were noises of a crowd of people talking and walking against a background of the handling of glasses and cutlery as if it was all coming from a dinner party. At first this might not have been that frightening. It became so when the Centre's director accosted her only neighbour to ask him about the late parties he was holding which were so noisy. To her amazement the neighbour replied that he was not holding any parties and that he too was hearing the same noises which he thought were coming from the Centre. It was then that Dr. Zolina began to attribute those noises to ghostly manifestations in which she did not believe until then. But had there been any doubts in her belief, these were dispelled when there began to materialize mysterious gusts of wind and banging of doors, with the barking of her dog which followed the pattern already shown of dogs always sensing the presence of ghosts. Both Dr. Zolina and her husband were now frightened and no one would have blamed them had they abandoned those premises once and for all. But their fear was overcome by a stronger determination to find a solution to their situation. By now they believed the house was being haunted by its original owner Sir Oliver Starkey so they tried to learn all they could about him. They said they had traced his will where it was found out that he had left monies for masses to be said for the repose of his soul, which probably enough were either never said or discontinued during the 400 years since his death. So the Centre's director and her husband paid their own money to have masses said regularly, and according to them, the manifestations calmed down. So much so that there is no more fear in that house, and the occupants say they consider the ghost that haunts it as a member of the family.

Both occupants are to be complimented for having dealt with this matter in the way they did. May the ghost haunting their premises be eventually subdued altogether. But until it is, it will feature as another ghost of Malta that may still be manifesting itself even now, at the time when I am writing about it.

Nothing of whatever has been put in this book is intended to convert sceptics. Indeed some of these may not be as sceptical as they appear to be. A popular gentleman who lived at Mdina had always showed a front of disbelief in ghosts when speaking in public. Yet now after his demise it came out how he had admitted to close friends that his house was haunted. And how he and his familiars often sensed the presence of a ghost and felt his touch on arms and shoulders without ever seeing him. However for all of us who are convinced of another life after death it should not be difficult to understand that ghostly manifestations imply the general survival of physical death by human personality. But then one cannot dismiss the many authentic hauntings which appear inexplicable by the light of contemporary knowledge of natural laws. It is therefore felt more than ever before that a proper and determined study of this section of the occult has become overdue. Until this is carried out whatever beliefs are changed or retained will stand to be swayed with the incessant oscillations of conjecture.

It is a likely good guess that if and when such a study is concluded Malta will have reached her zenith as a nation. But more in the way of a surety rather than a guess there is still the feeling that other than blue skies, the wonderful history and warm friendliness to pick the island out as a top attraction there will always be her ghosts.

Portraits of ghosts
drawn by a clairvoyant
(ref. page 189–190)

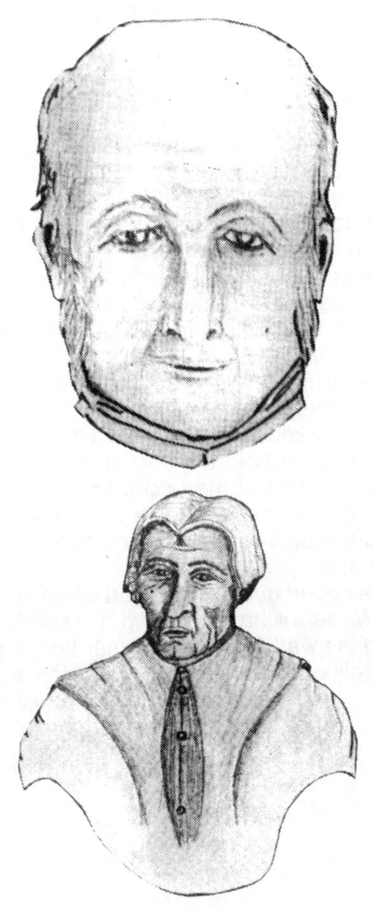

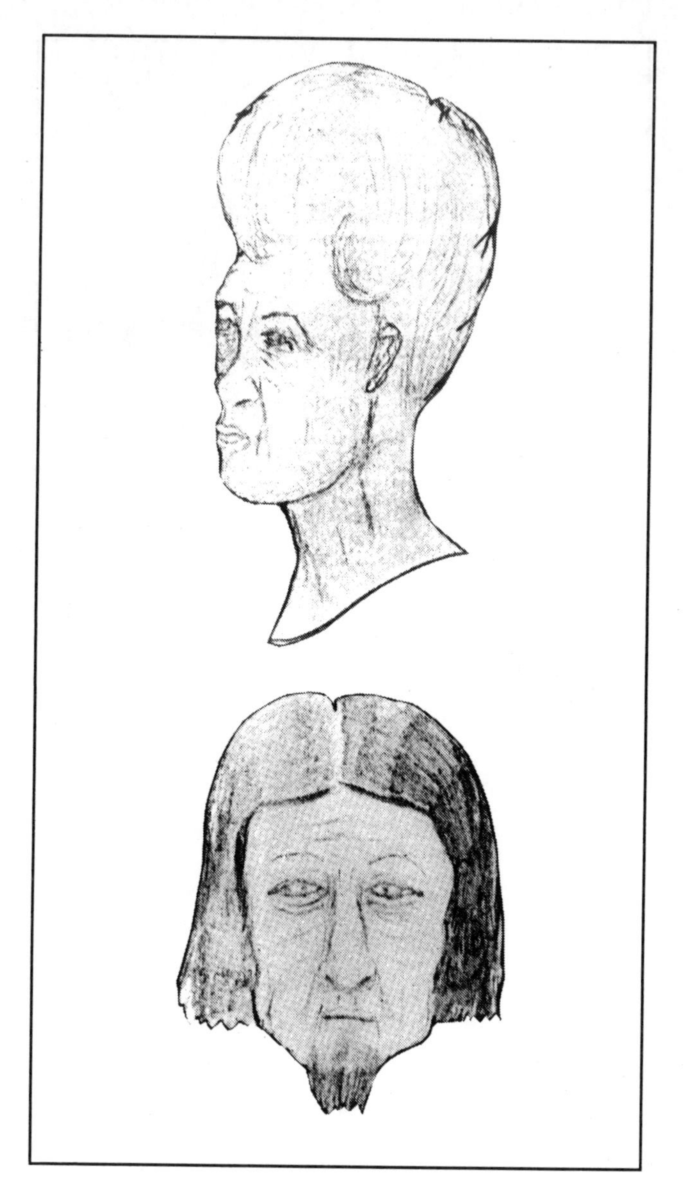